OUR LIVING WORLD OF NATURE

The
Life
of the
Mountains

Developed jointly with The World Book Encyclopedia

Produced with the cooperation of
The United States Department of the Interior

The Life of the Mountains

MAURICE BROOKS

Published in cooperation with
The World Book Encyclopedia

McGraw-Hill Book Company

NEW YORK   TORONTO   LONDON

MAURICE BROOKS *was born in mountainous West Virginia and has lived there for many years. He was educated at West Virginia University and the University of Michigan and has taught at the Universities of Virginia and Minnesota. Presently he is Professor of Wildlife Management at West Virginia University. For eight years he was a member of the West Virginia Conservation Commission, and he has also served as President of the Wilson Ornithological Society. Professor Brooks's interest in mountain ecology is in keeping with family tradition—his father and three of his brothers are professional naturalists or biologists. He himself has explored the Appalachian Mountains from Quebec to Georgia and is the author of the recent book* The Appalachians.

Library of Congress Catalog Card Number: 67–16307

890 NR 72

ISBN 07-008075-5

OUR LIVING WORLD OF NATURE

Science Editor

RICHARD B. FISCHER   *Cornell University*

Board of Consultants

ROLAND CLEMENT   *National Audubon Society*

C. GORDON FREDINE   *National Park Service, The United States Department of the Interior*

WILLIAM H. NAULT   *Field Enterprises Educational Corporation*

BENJAMIN NICHOLS   *Cornell University*

EUGENE P. ODUM   *University of Georgia*

HENRY J. OOSTING   *Duke University*

OLIN SEWALL PETTINGILL, JR.   *Cornell University*

DAVID PIMENTEL   *Cornell University*

PAUL B. SEARS   *Yale University*

ROBERT L. USINGER   *University of California*

Readability Consultant

JOSEPHINE PIEKARZ IVES   *New York University*

Special Consultant for The Life of the Mountains

ROBERT T. ORR   *California Academy of Sciences*

Contents

LIFE ON THE MOUNTAINS   9

*A bridge of living things 10;   A touch of Mexico 12;   Land of
the pygmy forest 14;   A giant step upward 20;   A bird
that walks underwater 23;   A visitor from Mexico 24;   In the
great pine forest 28;   Up steepening slopes 32;   Life in the
Douglasfir forest 35;   Birds in the fir forest 36;   Mammals
on the mountain 39;   The uppermost forest 44;   No trees
at all 46;   How timber-line trees get that way 50;   The
view from the top 53;   Animals of the summit 55;   Why
the San Franciscos? 56;   The seven zones of life 58;
The trouble with Merriam's system 60;   The upside-down
mountain 61;   A last look at the San Franciscos 62*

ANCIENT MOUNTAINS   67

*A closer look at eastern mountains 70;   What makes them
special 72;   New York's finest 73;   To the top of
Mount Marcy 79;   Let thrushes lead the way 80;   The
end of the trail 85;   South to the Appalachians 88;
On the slopes of Mount Le Conte 92;   A land where North
meets South 94;   Three peaks at the top 96;   An ecological
riddle 100;   In the valley of the big trees 102;   Routes
north and south 105;   The lure of the mountains 109*

ISLANDS IN THE SKY 111

How the butterflies found the mountaintops 112; Gifts of the glaciers 116; Bog islands 119; How the bogs became mixing pots 122; Where hares abound 123; Mountain turncoats 123; Boom and bust for snowshoe hares 125; Salamanders everywhere 132; A profusion of plethodons 133; What it all means 135; New trees from old 137; Western islands 138; How to visit Mexico without leaving the United States 143; A return to Canada 147

A VARIETY OF MOUNTAINS 149

Where hawks fly by 152; A day on Hawk Mountain 153; Midcontinent mountains 156; Land of many peaks 162; On Trail Ridge Road 167; On the mountain meadows 168; The northern Rockies 171; From the Sierras to Mount Rainier 178; On the mountain of ice 184; Mountains by the sea 189; From sea to summit 192; The spell of the mountains 196

APPENDIX

Mountains in the National Park System 203; Vanishing Wildlife of the Mountains 210; Basics of Backpacking 212; A Guide to Common Fossils 216

Glossary 221
Bibliography 226
Illustration Credits and Acknowledgments 227
Index 228

Life
on the Mountains

From a hundred miles away you begin to see them, sharp points rising into the Arizona sky. At every new vantage point you pause to scan the horizon for their familiar outlines, and as you draw nearer the glimpses become more frequent. Before long you notice that the separate peaks are united at their bases on a high plateau. You note that forests cover most of the lower slopes but the summits are treeless. If it is early summer, patches of snow may linger on the upper slopes, for these are the highest mountains in Arizona, the San Francisco Peaks.

Somehow the peaks seem to belong to the land, looking as classic mountains should look. The Coconino Plateau at their base stands well above sea level, as high as almost any land east of the Mississippi. Yet from this elevated base, the clean-lined profiles of the San Francisco Peaks soar upward still another six thousand feet or so, dominating the vast northern portion of Arizona. There is no doubt about it—you are looking at real mountains.

But you can be sure that you are not the first to be impressed by the grandeur and mysterious beauty of these peaks. Hopi Indians live nearby, and from their mesas the

San Franciscos are constantly in view. The Indians believe that these majestic summits are the home of their gods, or *kachinas*, the spirits that keep watch over an ancient people. Nor are the Hopis alone in their reverence for the peaks. The San Francisco Mountains are special places for outdoorsmen as well—biologists, geologists, hikers, skiers, and all others who are stirred by high places, fine scenery, and a wealth of living things.

A bridge of living things

Ecologists, the scientists who study the relations of living things to each other and to their environment, are especially impressed by the San Francisco Mountains. From their point of view, these Arizona mountains are practically unique. Because of a special set of circumstances, the San Franciscos form an ecological paradise.

Most important is the location of the mountains. Out of sight but only a couple of hundred miles to the south lies Mexico, with its Sonoran Desert, its lofty Sierra Madre, and its rich and varied plant and animal life. Many of the influences, as well as some of the inhabitants, of this neigh-

10

boring land have spilled across the border into the San Francisco Peaks area. Here you will discover many plants and animals that are more typical of Mexico than of the United States.

On the other hand, since the peaks reach elevations of twelve thousand feet and more, they also stand as isolated outposts of Canadian landscape. The uppermost slopes, beyond the line where trees will grow, are inhabited by many forms of life that would be equally at home around Hudson Bay in far-northern Canada. Many residents of the summits are *circumpolar* in distribution; they are found in arctic land areas throughout the Northern Hemisphere, and they use mountain peaks as stepping stones to the south.

On the intermediate slopes, the communities of living things change gradually with increasing elevation. Each small gain in altitude corresponds to a journey of several hundred miles to the north. By climbing the mountains, you can find a sampling of all the major life forms you might encounter if you were to travel the full span of the continent from Mexico to Canada. Thus the San Franciscos serve as a link, a bridge of living things that joins North with South. Little wonder, then, that ecologists find the area a place of pure magic.

Arizona's snow-capped San Francisco Peaks—the remains of a volcano that was active hundreds of thousands of years ago—dominate the Coconino Plateau north of Flagstaff. The smaller craters and cinder cones in the foreground also attest to the area's long history of volcanic activity.

11

A touch of Mexico

The best way to observe this layering of living things is by approaching the San Franciscos from the south. As you drive through the great cactus forest of southern Arizona, you will catch your first tantalizing glimpses of the peaks while they are still a hundred miles or more away.

Although not actually in the mountains, the great saguaro desert of south-central Arizona is definitely part of the San Francisco country. The Arizona desert is a northward extension of the elevated, generally arid Sonoran Plateau, most of which lies across the border in Mexico. Giant saguaro cactuses dot the landscape, some of them standing twenty-five to forty feet tall. Their massive columnar forms dominate the scene, yet many other plants are present: desert ironwood and other trees, shrubs such as mesquite and ocotillo, and a great many smaller plants, some of them covered with bright blossoms. Even so, plant life seems rather sparse. In this dry land, no plant can afford to crowd its neighbors.

Desert plants flourish in the arid lowlands well to the south of the San Francisco Peaks. Among them are the towering saguaro cactus and the yellow-blossoming paloverde, whose name—Spanish for "green stick"—refers to the shrub's emerald-colored bark.

Collared lizards live throughout the southwestern desert country, especially in areas where rocky rubble affords them quick refuge from intruders and shelter from the hot midday sun. These agile predatory reptiles often grow to about one foot in length.

If each one is to obtain sufficient moisture from the hard, caked soil, it must have plenty of growing space.

But if plant life is sparse, animals seem practically non-existent, at least during the heat of a summer afternoon. You may see a few birds and perhaps some butterflies and other insects. A lizard may dart for cover as you approach. But that is about all the animal activity you are likely to notice.

Where, you wonder, are all the animals? Puzzled, you slip into the slender shadow cast by a saguaro and wipe the perspiration from your forehead. And there you find the answer to your question: like yourself, most of the animals have sought refuge from the intense heat of midday. Some find shelter in underground burrows or in cavities in trees; others seek the shade beneath tangles of vegetation. Yet there is life, an amazing variety of it. Return after sundown, especially at dusk or dawn, and you will find the desert alive with animals, many of them representing species that have strayed north from Mexico.

Even by day, you can find a few traces of animal activity. The saguaro trunks are certain to be riddled with holes; these are the homes of gilded flickers, elf owls, and gila woodpeckers. The branching arms of some of the cactuses may also cradle the crude platform nests of red-tailed hawks or the smaller nests of white-winged doves. A roadrunner may dart across the hot soil, and sleek little Gambel's quail are likely to be slipping among the grasses and herbs as they search the desert floor for seeds.

If you venture into the tangled brush in a rocky ravine, you may encounter still larger animals: mule deer, jack rabbits, bobcats, skunks, and ringtails are all possibilities. If you are especially fortunate, you may even spot a coati, a long-tailed raccoonlike animal rarely found north of the Mexican border. Groups of peccaries, little wild native pigs, also seek the shade of thickets during the hours of greatest heat. Burrowing mice, ground squirrels, kit foxes, coyotes, snakes, and many other creatures spend the day resting in dens or beneath shrubs where they can escape the burning sun.

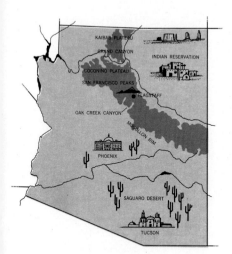

The San Francisco Peaks, the tallest mountains in Arizona, stand on the high plateau that angles across the north-central part of the state. By approaching the mountains from the saguaro desert to the south, a visitor can easily observe the effects of increasing elevation on plant life in the area.

Land of the pygmy forest

It is tempting to remain in the cactus desert and explore its wealth of intriguing plants and animals, but the San Francisco Peaks are shimmering on the horizon. As you head north, they become more prominent and lure you steadily onward. Slowly but surely you gain in elevation as you approach the mountains, for the desert is rimmed by higher land.

As the altitude increases, you will notice subtle changes in the communities of plants and animals on either side of the highway. One by one, various species disappear from the scene and are replaced by new trees, new birds, and new mammals. The giant saguaros, for example, become dwarfed on higher slopes, and finally they disappear altogether. After passing through a region where the most prominent plants are the large yuccas known as Spanish bayonet, you begin to notice more and more gnarled low-growing evergreens. Finally you reach an elevation where the land is nearly covered with these dwarfed trees, the junipers and pinyon

Twisted, gnarled pinyon pines are the dominant tree of the "pygmy forest" that flourishes at intermediate elevations in the Southwest. Although capable of growing to a height of fifty feet, most pinyon pines are much shorter. This one is on the brink of the Grand Canyon.

14

pines. Their contorted forms clothe every slope and canyon wall with masses of rich, dark green foliage.

The air is cooler on these heights, and the increasing number of permanent streams hints at a more dependable supply of water. The plants, too, grow somewhat closer together than in the cactus forest, for here the competition for moisture is less intense. For miles around, the slopes are covered by low-growing pinyons and junipers. Vast areas of the Southwest, where the land lies between about five and seven thousand feet above sea level, are covered by this so-called pygmy forest.

It was in this area that many of the prehistoric Indian tribes built their communal "apartment houses," either underneath overhanging cliffs or in recesses in canyon walls. Notable Indian ruins in the San Francisco country, such as Montezuma Castle and the dwellings at Walnut Canyon, are preserved by the National Park Service and are well worth a visit. The Indians used pinyons and junipers both for timbers in their dwellings and as firewood. The resinous wood, which gives off a pungent aroma when it burns, still is favored by many campers. But the pinyons were even more important to the Indians as a source of food, for small edible nuts cling tightly between the scales of

Young pinyon cones (*top*) reach a length of one to two inches by the end of their first year of growth (*left*). At this stage, two to thirty nutlike seeds are maturing between the cone scales. Later, the scales spread apart, the seeds drop to the ground, and the empty cones (*bottom*) soon fall from the tree.

the cones. In years when the nuts are plentiful, Indians still harvest millions of pounds of the sweet, nutritious seeds.

Birds and mammals of the pinyon-juniper forest also depend on the nuts. Wherever pinyon pines grow, raucous pinyon jays are certain to be present, competing for a share of the harvest. These dull blue, crestless jays, which look something like miniature crows, characteristically move about in flocks, searching the trees and the ground beneath them for nuts. The noisy, conspicuous pinyon jays are so much a part of the pygmy forest that you will learn to look for them as soon as you enter their territory.

Big gray rock squirrels also are characteristic of the pinyon-juniper zone. Although they have long, bushy tails like those of tree squirrels and can climb when they want to, rock squirrels spend most of their time on the ground and build their nests in rocky crevices. Several smaller species of ground squirrels and other rodents also flourish there, living on the bounty provided by pine nuts. Hawks, owls, weasels, skunks, foxes, and other predators that abound in the pinyon-juniper forest prey, in turn, on the plentiful supply of rodents.

Robin-sized pinyon jays are found throughout the pinyon-juniper forest, where they congregate in noisy, ever-moving flocks. The birds forage among the branches and on the ground beneath the trees in an endless search for pinyon nuts, juniper berries, and insects.

17

WALNUT CANYON
NATIONAL MONUMENT

Walnut Canyon, a
four-hundred-foot-deep,
twenty-mile-long crack in the
edge of the Coconino Plateau,
lies a few miles southeast of
the San Francisco Peaks. Five
centuries before Columbus set
sail for the New World, the
canyon supported a bustling
Indian community which, at its
height, included more than
three hundred separate
dwellings. The apartments were
built on shelves high on the
canyon wall where wind and
rain had eroded deep crevices
in soft layers of limestone.

Living conditions in the canyon
were good. Water was available
at the canyon floor; corn,
squash, and beans were
cultivated on the plateau above;
and the surrounding forest
supplied the Indians with
pinyon nuts, firewood, and
building timber. Even so, after
two hundred years of
occupation the community at
Walnut Canyon was
mysteriously abandoned. Today
its ruins are preserved as a
national monument.

A giant step upward

As you cross the semiarid lowlands on your approach to the peaks, you will eventually discern a great obstacle on the northern horizon. Just ahead of you, the land rises nearly two thousand feet in abrupt cliffs. This is the Mogollon Rim, the edge of the flat upland known as the Coconino Plateau, which forms the base of the San Francisco Mountains.

The only way to scale this barrier is to seek one of the few canyons carved by streams across the edge of the Mogollon Rim. One of the best routes is through Oak Creek Canyon. Once you enter the canyon, you will find a lush new world, for canyons in mountain country are havens for an unexpected variety of life. All about the mouth of Oak Creek Canyon and up the slopes to the top of the Mogollon Rim, the typical vegetation is pinyon-juniper forest. But in the

The red sandstone walls of Oak Creek Canyon form a colorful backdrop for the autumn foliage of broadleaf trees that flourish beside Oak Creek. Because of cooler air and plentiful moisture, living conditions in the canyon contrast sharply with those on the dry surrounding slopes.

canyon itself plants and wildlife are entirely different.

In the first place, there is running water. Equally important, currents of cool, moisture-laden air flow perpetually down through the canyon from the snowy summits of the San Francisco Peaks. These currents are heavier than the surrounding masses of warm air, and as a result they lie close to the ground and go swirling down through gaps such as Oak Creek Canyon. The cool, moist air moderates the semidesert conditions usually found at these altitudes and permits the survival of plants and animals not normally found at such low elevations.

Thus canyons result in interruptions in the orderly layering of life forms that we have been observing in mountain country. They harbor an interesting mixture of plants and animals that may be a bit confusing at first but is all the more intriguing for being unexpected.

In mountainous areas throughout the West, swift-flowing streams attract pert starling-sized dippers, birds that are famous for their habit of plunging directly into torrents to forage for insects and small fish. Dippers build bulky ovenlike nests of moss, pine needles, and other plant materials, often located so close to the rushing stream that the outer surfaces of the nests are constantly wet.

A bird that walks underwater

When you enter the canyon and begin to climb along the highway that winds upward beside Oak Creek, you are struck immediately by the effects of moisture and cool air in a semidesert land. Instead of junipers and pinyon pines, the creek is lined by verdant stands of willows, sycamores, alders, ashes, and other broadleaf trees.

All about you there are brightly colored birds. Summer tanagers and Bullock's orioles flit through the treetops. Black phoebes dart after insects along the stream. And every opening blossom is visited by black-chinned hummingbirds in search of nectar and insects. As you gain in elevation, still other species appear. Western tanagers, red-shafted flickers, painted redstarts, and other birds begin to mingle with the species you saw nearer the mouth of the canyon.

But the most fascinating bird to be found in the canyon is the water ouzel, or dipper. Found from Alaska to Panama, this neat little bird flourishes wherever it can find tumbling mountain streams; the swifter and wilder the water, the better the dipper seems to like it.

Look for the dipper at the foot of a cascade, or perched on a rock projecting from the white water of a rapid. You may not notice it at first, for the dipper's body is an inconspicuous slate gray and its head is dull brown. But you are certain to recognize it by its habit of constantly bobbing its body up and down, a motion so characteristic that it is responsible for the dipper's name.

More often than not you will hear the dipper before you see it. Like its near relatives the wrens, the dipper is a notable songster. It sings loud and long, pouring out cascades of clear, ringing notes. Winter or summer, night or day, it makes no difference to the dipper—when it wants to sing, it sings. On a moonless January midnight in British Columbia, with a temperature of forty degrees below zero, the dipper sings as joyously as it would on a balmy morning in May along Oak Creek.

The dipper's most notable habit, however, is its manner of feeding. It captures the bulk of its food on the stream bottom, under the water. Regardless of the force of the current, the dipper plunges fearlessly into the water and walks about on the stream bed, foraging among the rocks and pebbles for aquatic insects and other succulent morsels. When it emerges, its water-repellent feathers are still sleek and dry.

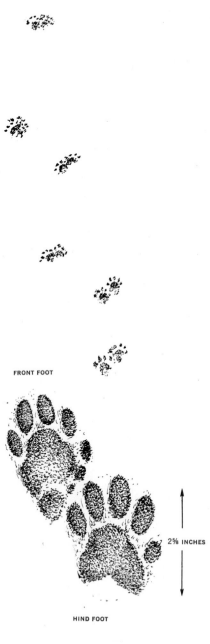

FRONT FOOT

2⅞ INCHES

HIND FOOT

A visitor from Mexico

Another specialty of Oak Creek Canyon is the colorful red-faced warbler, a bird that lives mainly in the mountains of Mexico and farther south. So far as we know, Oak Creek Canyon is the northernmost limit of its breeding range. It nests in the forests of pine and Douglasfir that flourish on the cool, moist slopes near the head of the canyon.

Many of the wood warblers are colorful birds, but the red-faced warbler is one of the best. When you hear its insectlike, not particularly musical call and look up into the Douglasfir overhead, you won't believe your eyes. The male's body is a subtle combination of pearly grays, but its face, throat, and upper breast are brilliant red. A black hood across its crown provides the finishing touch. As you watch this beautiful sprite flitting from bough to bough, you will understand why some of our Spanish-American neighbors make no distinction between wood warblers and butterflies, but call them all "mariposas."

Of course you will see butterflies in the canyon as well: big swallowtails, sulphur butterflies, and a number of other showy species that hover around the bright flowers growing beside the creek. In this otherwise arid land, the shaded banks of the stream also provide refuge for toads, frogs, and a few salamanders. Mammals live in the canyon too, but most of them are too shy to reveal their presence. Around picnic areas, you are certain to see chipmunks and ground squirrels, some of them bold enough to take peanuts from an outstretched hand. Mule deer also venture down to the creek in the morning and evening, but they are wary and usually flee at your approach.

With luck, you may even find the tracks of a ringtail, one of the Southwest's most attractive mammals. But do not expect to see the cats themselves, for these long-tailed raccoonlike creatures remain in hiding during the day. They haunt rocky slopes and steep ravines, usually near water, and venture out only after dark, when they hunt for rodents, insects, fruits, and berries.

The ringtail is very much at home in canyon country, where it sleeps the day away in hollow logs, on sheltered rock ledges, or even in untenanted summer cabins. After dark, this rare cat-sized mammal emerges from hiding to hunt for small rodents, birds, insects, fruits, and berries.

Seldom seen in the United States, red-faced warblers are among the most attractive of the predominantly Central American birds whose ranges extend just barely north of the Mexican border. The warblers are found at altitudes up to nine thousand feet, but they also breed in cool, well-watered canyons at lower elevations. Their inconspicuous nests, constructed of grasses and bark fibers, are hidden under trees and in grassy thickets. Mature birds of both sexes have vivid red heads; on younger birds the facial feathers tend more toward pinkish shades.

In the great pine forest

At the head of Oak Creek Canyon, on top of the Mogollon Rim, the landscape once again changes abruptly. Here on the Coconino Plateau, the heights above sea level average about six thousand feet, about four thousand feet higher than at the beginning of your journey in the saguaro forest. By now the San Francisco Peaks seem almost within reach; their jagged summits loom like walls against the near horizon.

Once again, you cannot fail to be impressed by the effects of increasing altitude, for on the plateau you enter a new kind of country. On every suitable site, the land is covered by a vast forest of ponderosa pines. From Oak Creek Canyon on the south to the North Rim of the Grand Canyon and beyond, this forest extends with few interruptions for almost two hundred miles north and south. It is the finest stand of ponderosa pines in North America.

One of the first things you will notice is the sparsity of undergrowth: the forest looks like a man-made park. The trees are not huge by Pacific Coast standards, and the forest

Multitudes of showy coneflowers spangle the rain-drenched expanse of an opening in the ponderosa pine forest on Arizona's Coconino Plateau. This pleasant parklike country, more than a mile above sea level, is typical of the region surrounding the San Francisco Peaks.

crown is only about a hundred feet above the ground. But the trees are well spaced, and their massive trunks rise straight up. Unless there has been a fire or some other disturbance, the ground will be littered with cones and a deep accumulation of pine needles that spring gently beneath your feet. The forest floor is dappled with patches of sunlight that beams down through the open crowns of the trees, and gentle breezes rustle through the needles high overhead. The total effect is one of calm and serenity.

And then you realize—perhaps it is too peaceful. Where are all the animals? The fact is that relatively few kinds of animals are able to find food and shelter in a pure stand of any tree species. Any animals that live in the ponderosa pine forest in the Coconino area must be able to make their homes in the pines themselves, on the sparsely covered ground beneath the trees, or in burrows in the root-choked soil. Their food must be pine seeds, pine needles, underground fungi, or insects that parasitize ponderosa pines.

Yet there is life in such a forest. Stop for a moment and listen. Now and then birds call from the branches overhead. If you remain quiet, they soon will come near enough to be seen.

Loose bands of pygmy nuthatches flit among the branches, endlessly searching for insects on every limb and in every crevice in the bark. Like all nuthatches, these active little gymnasts scurry headfirst down the tree trunks as easily as they climb up. Mountain chickadees, with conspicuous white lines above their eyes, whistle and sing with calls that resemble the songs of their eastern relatives. Colorful Audubon's and Grace's warblers also live in the ponderosa pines.

One of the showiest birds of the ponderosa pine forest is the handsome Steller's jay, feathered in blues so intense that they appear almost black. These large crested jays move about in groups, sometimes in the treetops and sometimes on the ground, working over pine cones for any seeds that may have been overlooked by other creatures of the forest.

In openings among the trees you can also expect to see broad-tailed hummingbirds, especially if flowers such as scarlet gilia and scarlet penstemon are in bloom. For some reason, bright red flowers seem to be irresistible to hummingbirds; they swarm like bees around the blossoms and drink the nectar hidden in the blooms. If several of the broad-tailed hummingbirds are active in the same area, you will be surprised by the continuous chorus of shrill clicking sounds

The trumpet-shaped blossoms of scarlet gilia normally are vivid red, although some plants bear pink, orange, or white flowers. Its other name, "polecat plant," results from the skunklike odor given off when the leaves are crushed.

29

Mantled with autumn snow, the San Franciscos loom high beyond a forest of ponderosa pines.

that the males make with their wings. In late June, rufous hummingbirds also are present on the San Francisco slopes, the males with foxy backs and brilliant scarlet throats.

The forest harbors mule deer, various kinds of mice, and other animals as well. But the most characteristic mammals of the ponderosa pine forest are the tassel-eared squirrels. They live almost exclusively among ponderosa pines, and are found from the Coconino Plateau eastward to the Sangre de Cristo Mountains in New Mexico and northward to southern Utah and northern Colorado.

Among the largest of our tree squirrels, tassel-eared squirrels are in many ways the most attractive. The name itself is descriptive: their ears are long and end in tufts of blackish hairs that are especially conspicuous in winter. Although all the tassel-eared squirrels are similar in general appearance, two different species are found in this general area. Abert's squirrels, which live south of the Grand Canyon, have white bellies and tails that are whitish only on the underside. In contrast, their relatives on the Kaibab Plateau, north of the Grand Canyon, have black bellies and tails that are almost entirely white. Tassel-eared squirrels on the plateau are known as Kaibab squirrels. Scientists speculate that formation of the canyon presented an impassable barrier to migrations between the two populations. As a result, each group has evolved the differences we see today.

Up steepening slopes

On the approach to a mountain, all roads lead upward. All across the Coconino Plateau, the terrain gains slowly but steadily in elevation. Once you pass the Flagstaff area, however, the hills along the highway steepen abruptly: you are beginning your ascent up the flanks of the San Francisco Mountains. The peaks that had seemed so distant at the start of your journey across the desert now tower directly in front of you. Their rocky masses dominate the landscape so completely that you feel dwarfed as you stand at their base and gaze at the summits several thousand feet above you.

The easy way to climb a mountain—riding on an aerial tramway—can reveal breathtaking vistas not visible to the hiker or motorist. The setting here is Sandia Peak, near Albuquerque, New Mexico.

32

The best way to learn of the life on a mountain is to climb its slopes on foot. Dozens of trails thread through the forests of the San Francisco Peaks. But in many places the trails are steep and travel is rugged. Hiking, moreover, requires stamina and time, more time perhaps than you can spare. Thus, if you are like most people, you probably will choose to drive up to the Arizona Snow Bowl at about nine thousand feet. From this famous winter sports area you can ride a ski lift, which even in summer will whisk you up to 11,800 feet. You will have an easy walk from the top of the ski lift to the summit.

If you make the ascent by auto and ski lift, you are certain to miss many details of plant and animal life, but this method does offer a good many advantages. A few mountain creatures, such as the blue grouse, are more easily observed from an automobile than from the ground. And a sampling procedure, involving frequent stops and quick excursions on foot, allows for considerable coverage in a minimum of time. The ride on the ski lift, moreover, carries you above the treetops, providing a perspective that the hiker misses completely. You have a fine vantage point for spotting game animals, especially deer and perhaps an occasional bear.

Whatever your means of ascent, the journey begins in the ponderosa pine forest of the Coconino Plateau. Although you are now climbing steadily upward, you will detect few changes in the forest until you reach an elevation of around eight thousand feet. Then things begin to change rather quickly. Mingled here and there with the ponderosa pines, especially on north-facing slopes, are a few Douglasfirs, readily distinguished by the thick, deeply furrowed bark on their trunks. In addition, their needles are short, and the branches arch slightly upward at the tips. The trunks of the ponderosa pines, in contrast, are covered with brittle platelike scales of bark; the open crowns seem rather coarse; and the clustered needles are five to ten inches long. Douglasfir cones also are distinctive, with long, ragged three-pronged tabs projecting from between the scales.

The higher you climb, the more Douglasfirs you see. Ponderosa pines become less prominent, until only a few stragglers remain on warm, south-facing slopes. By the time you reach nine thousand feet, Douglasfirs have taken over as the principal forest tree. The transition has been gradual, for here, as in most other areas, there are no abrupt changes in plant cover, no rigid boundaries that seem to say "this

Three-pronged tabs projecting from between the cone scales positively identify the Douglasfir. Each cone scale conceals two single-winged seeds that will be scattered by the wind.

far and no farther." Almost imperceptibly one type of forest gives way to another as soil, exposure, and weather conditions change.

Life in the Douglasfir forest

Although Douglasfirs are the dominant trees at these elevations, they do not grow in pure stands. Mixed with the firs are limber pines and aspens; the pines actually are intermingled with the firs, but the aspens tend to grow in isolated patches. If they are to survive, aspen seedlings require plenty of sunlight, more than reaches the forest floor beneath a dense stand of evergreens. But in areas where the coniferous forest has been disturbed by fire or lumbering operations, aspens are almost certain to take over.

As they mature, the aspens add a great deal of color and variety to the mountainscape. Most obvious, even from a distance, is their color. Firs and other conifers are cloaked in somber greens throughout the year. But in autumn, when early frosts come to the mountain slopes, the cooler, softer greens of the aspens are transformed almost overnight into masses of bright golden yellow and occasionally even flaming scarlet.

More important, a greater variety of ferns and wild flowers can grow in the light shade beneath the aspens than in the heavy shade beneath a mature stand of firs. Throughout the summer, openings among the aspens are bright with dainty blue gentians, cinquefoil, western bluebells, geums, and other flowers. Especially common are Canada violets, which grow just as vigorously in the San Franciscos as in the Green Mountains of Vermont. Columbines, saxifrages, and mountain-dwelling heaths also are abundant. The columbines, in particular, are frequently visited by hummingbirds.

Aspen stands, which sometimes cover entire mountainsides, are particularly good places to look for animals. The high San Francisco slopes support a large population of mule deer, magnificent game animals that are slightly larger

Stands of aspens take a foothold wherever clearings have been created in the dense mountainside forest of evergreens. The two-inch oval leaves, here seen in autumn gold, are set to fluttering by the slightest breeze.

35

In contrast to the gloom of the Douglasfir forest, aspen groves are light and airy, permitting wild flowers and other plants to flourish about the bases of the trees.

than eastern white-tailed deer. During the day they take cover in shady places, enduring the plague of biting flies as best they can, but at twilight they become active and begin to feed. Like many other animals, mule deer tend to congregate in and about the edges of aspen stands and other openings in the evergreen forest. Grasses, legumes, low shrubs, and other foods are more plentiful here than in the fir forest, yet the shelter of the evergreens is near at hand.

This tendency of deer and other animals to be more abundant in areas where two different kinds of plant cover meet and merge is widespread in all natural habitats. The phenomenon is so important, in fact, that ecologists have a special name for it: they call it *edge effect*.

Birds in the fir forest

Major types of vegetation each tend to shelter different kinds of grouse, fine game birds that are distantly related to the domestic chicken. There are prairie chickens in the grasslands, for example, sage grouse in sagebrush country, ruffed grouse in eastern deciduous forests, and ptarmigan in arctic lands. Western coniferous forests, especially where Douglas-fir abounds, are no exception. In this case, the characteristic species is the blue grouse, a wide-ranging species found all the way from southern Alaska to southern California and east to the Dakotas and New Mexico.

Not actually blue, males of these large grouse are predominantly slate gray flecked with black and brown. The males also have a bright orange comb over each eye. Females and young, on the other hand, tend to be brownish in overall appearance. The total effect of such coloring is to make the birds nearly invisible, for their mottled plumage blends perfectly with their forest surroundings.

Mule deer are common along the edges of aspen groves and meadows in the mountain forest. This buck is still "in velvet." Later in the season the downy covering on its antlers will be rubbed off against trees and rocks.

With its tail feathers spread in a broad fan and its colorful throat sacs in full display, a blue grouse cock enacts its courtship ritual, strutting to attract a mate. The female later will brood a clutch of seven to ten eggs in a nest lined with pine needles.

Since the San Franciscos are near the southern limit of their range, blue grouse are less common here than they are farther north. But you will find them on the San Francisco Peaks if you know when and where to look. The best time is early morning, just about sunrise, although they become active again in the early evening. The best places are along the margins of roads and trails in mixed aspen-Douglasfir country—another example of edge effect. The birds feed on seeds and berries of plants growing in the brushy borders of these openings in the forest canopy.

Curiously, you will have better luck observing the birds if you travel by car rather than on foot. Feeding grouse pay little heed to passing or even pausing automobiles. You can easily drive within a few feet of the birds and stop to photograph or observe them at leisure. The grouse simply ignore you. But if you step out of the car, no matter how cautiously, the birds are likely to flee immediately, flying or running for the shelter of trees.

In one way, blue grouse are nearly unique among American birds. They migrate *down* the mountain in spring and summer, and do their courting, mating, and nesting on the lower slopes. When snow begins to fly in autumn, they return to higher ground, where they feed on fir needles and buds and find shelter in the natural tents formed by snow-laden branches of the evergreens. There may be a few other birds in the Northern Hemisphere that move northward or to higher elevations in winter, but such behavior is certainly exceptional.

Many of the other birds found in the aspen-fir forest also live in Canada. There are three-toed woodpeckers, brown creepers, ruby-crowned kinglets, red crossbills, pine siskins, and many others that you might as easily expect to find in New Brunswick, northern Minnesota, or the Canadian Rockies. The place may be Arizona, and cactuses may flourish only a few miles away, but in terms of climate and vegetation the upper slopes of the San Franciscos are genuine outposts of Canadian landscape. Because the habitat is suitable, the birds remain here instead of flying north to Canada. Although the birds mentioned above are found also in eastern forests, the San Franciscos, of course, provide homes for many strictly western species as well, such as Townsend's solitaires, western tanagers, mountain chickadees, and Steller's jays.

Mammals on the mountain

All the large mammals of the Douglasfir forest on the San Francisco Peaks are widely distributed in the West, and most are not restricted to the mountains. Mule deer, for example, are equally at home in the desert as long as there is a dependable water supply nearby. Mountain lions —also known as panthers, painters, pumas, and cougars— are found here, but they too roam the deserts and lowlands. Although these big, graceful cats are found in many places in the West, they are so rare and wary that you are unlikely to sight one. Even so, you may be fortunate enough to discover a mountain lion's tracks or a place where one of the cats has partially buried the uneaten carcass of a mule deer, its principal prey.

Grizzlies are no longer found in the San Franciscos, but the fir-aspen forest is a good place to be on the lookout for the black bear, another animal that ranges far and wide through mountain country. Don't be confused if some of the bears you see are brown or tan, since black bears are

In winter, blue grouse find both shelter and food among the branches of Douglasfirs. The boughs, bent by the weight of snow, protect the grouse from wind and cold; needles and buds provide their major source of food.

Mountain lions once were common all across America, but relentless pressure from hunters, bounty collectors, and stockmen has eliminated them from much of their former range. Today, the big cats hold their own primarily in the mountain wilderness of the West.

not necessarily black. As a matter of fact, light-colored bears actually outnumber black ones in many western areas. So far zoologists have been unable to determine why this should be true in the West but not in the East, where brown or tan bears are definitely unusual.

One of the genuine rarities seen from time to time on the upper San Francisco slopes is the spectacular bighorn, or mountain sheep. Again, these handsome animals are not restricted to any particular elevation. Some live in low-lying cactus deserts, and others range well up toward the mountain summits. They are seldom seen in dense forest, however. Bighorns prefer open areas and rough, rocky slopes where they can watch for approaching predators, such as mountain lions, and escape by fleeing over rugged terrain.

Scattered populations of bighorns are found throughout the West, from Alaska to Mexico, but the sheep in different areas vary in color. Alaskan bighorns, known as Dall's sheep, are white, while the more familiar Rocky Mountain bighorns are furred in shades of brown and tan. In Arizona and to the south, the so-called desert bighorns take on the pale grays and sand tones of their desert habitat.

Whatever their color, all bighorns are similar in form, and all are superbly adapted to life in rough country. An adult ram may stand three to three and one-half feet

40

high at the shoulder and weigh as much as three hundred pounds. Females are slightly smaller and much less stocky in build. The crowning glory of these animals is their horns. On females and immature males, the horns are short, slender, and almost straight. But those of an adult ram are truly massive, sometimes curving in a full circle, like earmuffs, on either side of his head. Rams use their horns as weapons in autumnal mating battles; they charge head-on and often collide with an impact that leaves both combatants dazed and slightly wobbly on their feet.

One of the most important adaptations of these handsome mountaineers is the structure of their feet. As on cows, each hoof is divided into two parts. When the sheep walk or jump, the two halves of the hoof spread apart, permitting the rigid outer edges to fit securely against uneven surfaces. As a further adaptation to mountain life, the underside of the hoof is fitted with a cushiony pad that provides excellent traction as the sheep run across smooth rocks. Thus

Black bears, which seldom exceed six hundred pounds in weight, are both the smallest and the commonest of our native bears. As this mother and her cubs demonstrate, black bears are not necessarily black; other possible colors include red-brown, tan, and even creamy white.

Among the most spectacular of
our native mammals are
bighorns, or mountain sheep.
These rare denizens of
wilderness areas are found in
scattered bands both on high
mountain slopes and in
low-lying deserts, from Alaska
all the way south into Mexico.
Several forms of the big sheep
exist. The white Dall's sheep
(*upper right*) is found only in
Alaska; the chestnut animal
(*center*) is characteristic of
the Rocky Mountains; the
sand-colored variety (*bottom*)
dwells in more southerly desert
areas.

Before the arrival of white
settlers, an estimated one
million bighorns roamed the
West. But by the beginning of
the twentieth century, only a
few thousand individuals were
left. Overhunting, competition
from range animals, and
diseases spreading from
domestic sheep all have taken
their toll. Conservationists now
are working to save these
handsome animals from the
threat of extinction.

equipped, the bighorns move fearlessly across steep, rugged slopes, nimbly leaping from rock to rock. Heights hold no terror for the big sheep, which seem to be most at home when they are feeding or resting on narrow ledges that project from the faces of abrupt cliffs.

The uppermost forest

The higher you climb on the San Francisco slopes, the cooler the air becomes. At the beginning of your journey in the saguaro desert, the thermometer may have stood at one hundred degrees or more. But by the time you reach the upper slopes, a sweater may be in order if you hope to remain comfortable.

As you might expect, plant life is affected by the changing climate. Along the steep trails near the top of the mountain, Douglasfir gradually becomes less prominent in the forest. Two species you have not seen before—Engelmann spruce and foxtail pine—begin to take over as the dominant trees. Engelmann spruce is a characteristic tree of high mountain slopes from British Columbia all the way to the Mexican border, while foxtail pine is most abundant on tall mountains in Colorado, Utah, and Nevada.

Although the kinds of trees may be different, this high-altitude woodland is very much like the forests that thrive all the way across Canada from Labrador to Alaska. Little wonder, then, that you need a sweater, for you have entered a true subarctic region, and the plants and animals demonstrate this fact.

Of the few mammals that live throughout the year on these heights, the porcupines, famous for their bristling armament of quills, are most characteristic. These large, ungainly rodents usually go unobserved since they are most active at night, yet there may be conspicuous signs of their presence. Despite their lumbering gait on the ground, porcupines are expert climbers. They gnaw the bark off tree trunks and branches in order to get at the nutritious growing layers just underneath. Foxtail pines seem to be among their favorite foods. Sometimes a porcupine will remain for days in a single tree, and when it finally moves on, broken branches and great raw scars on the trunk will testify to its voracious appetite.

FOXTAIL PINE

The foxtail pine, so called because of the dense, brushlike arrangement of its needles, is a characteristic tree of high-altitude forests on many western mountains. The sharp tips on its cone scales are responsible for its other common name, bristlecone pine. Some of these trees, estimated to be four thousand years old, are the oldest living things on earth.

44

In open, grassy areas here and on up to the summit, you are likely to notice another creature typical of the heights, the bird known as the water pipit. Except for the fact that the outermost feather on each side of its tail is white, this small bird, streaked with dull browns, is rather inconspicuous. Like most other ground-dwelling birds, the water pipit walks rather than hops. Another identifying characteristic is its habit of constantly dipping its tail and body up and down.

But the most interesting thing about the pipit is that you can expect to find it here at all. Water pipits are a genuine boreal species; they live in far-northern areas throughout the world and venture south only along the crests of high mountains. Northern Russia or western Arizona—it makes no difference to the water pipit, as long as it can find the proper set of living conditions.

The fearless porcupine turns its back on danger—and reveals a formidable array of up to thirty thousand sharp, barbed quills! Even so, mountain lions and bobcats manage to foil the porky's defense system by adroitly flipping the animal on its back and attacking its unprotected belly.

No trees at all

Near the summit of the mountain, you will come eventually to *timber line*, or *tree line*, the point beyond which trees are unable to grow. Below this line, providing soil conditions are right, forests flourish as they would on level land. But beyond timber line, living conditions are simply too harsh for trees of any sort to survive.

There is no abrupt change in living conditions, of course. If you imagine that arriving at timber line in any way resembles stepping from a tall forest into a clearing, you could not be further from the truth. Yet, if the mountain is high enough, the approach to timber line is inevitable with every

foot of increase in elevation. On the lowest slopes in the San Francisco region, saguaros eventually were replaced by pinyon pines and junipers as conditions became unsuitable for cactuses. The pinyon-juniper forest in turn gave way to ponderosa pines, then to Douglasfir, and finally to Engelmann spruce and foxtail pine. In every case, the shift from one type of vegetation to another was slow but noticeable; here, too, the transition from forest to no trees at all is gradual.

Anyone approaching timber line cannot help noticing the signs of more rigorous living conditions. For one thing, trees near the mountaintop are much shorter than those on the lower slopes. The forest also becomes somewhat less dense.

A panorama high in the Colorado Rockies clearly shows timber line, the ragged boundary beyond which trees cannot grow. The location of timber line does not depend on altitude alone: on warm, south-facing slopes and in sheltered ravines, the trees edge higher up the mountainsides; in more exposed sites they give way to tundra lower on the slopes.

As you climb still higher, you notice that more and more of the trees have short and twisted trunks, contorted forms hinting of a relentless struggle to survive.

Here and there a tree projects above its neighbors. But it looks lopsided: almost all the branches grow from one side of the trunk. With gales raging periodically across the heights, the branches grow much longer on the side away from the prevailing winds. This *flagging*, as it is called, is typical of timber-line trees throughout the world.

People sometimes jump to the conclusion that the wind actually bends the growing branches of such trees, but the causes of flagging are a good deal more complex. In the first place, constant breezes speed up the evaporation of water from buds on the windward side of the trunk. As a result, many of them become so dried out that they fail to grow. In addition, winter gales frequently pepper the buds with sharp

With the approach to timber line, the trees become contorted and stunted in their growth. Flagging (*below*) hints of the direction of the prevailing wind. Browned tips on the trees (*opposite*) result from the freezing of tender shoots that protruded above the protective blanket of the preceding winter's snow.

granules of sleet and frozen snow, while summer winds blast them with bits of sand. Again, the buds are so badly injured that they fail to grow into twigs. Branches on the more sheltered, leeward side of the trunk, in contrast, grow more or less normally. This accounts for the one-sided, wind-blown appearance of so many of the trees just below timber line.

Soon even these ragged sentinels disappear, and you find yourself treading through a forest of dwarfs—dense shrubby-looking spruces and pines with twisted trunks that grow perhaps waist high and in some places reach barely to your knees. Every low-lying, protected spot among the rocks is filled with these midgets; they grow in such compact masses that it is often possible to walk across the top of this strange timber-line forest. A bit farther up the slope there are no trees at all, just grasses, sedges, and herbs.

SUMMER

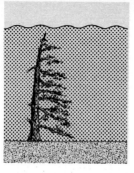

WINTER

SUMMER

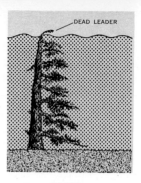

WINTER

The stunted form of timber-line trees results largely from the severity of winters on the upper mountain slopes. As long as a tree is covered by an insulating blanket of snow in winter, its upward growth is unimpeded. But when it grows tall enough for its tender growing tip, or leader, to project above the snow, the tip is killed by cold, drying gales. In summer a new leader replaces the dead one, but that too is killed the following winter. Thus, as the tree grows older, its trunk grows thicker and its branches continue to elongate, but its upward growth is halted.

How timber-line trees get that way

Timber line is the tension zone, a place of constant struggle. Although the trees are small, many of them are older than some of the forest giants on the lower slopes. Certain timber-line trees in fact rank among the oldest of all living things. But their growth is so slow that annual rings on cut stumps generally are just about indistinguishable and are visible only under magnification.

The shapes of the trees also testify to the harshness of living conditions. Many of the trees are conspicuously flagged, with most of the growth on the leeward sides of their trunks. The long lowermost branches creep almost like vines across the ground. Their dwarfed form, on the other hand, is governed by the amount of snow that accumulates at timber line each winter. During the first few years of its life, a timber-line tree grows slowly, but more or less normally, although it may already show evidence of flagging. In winter, a thick blanket of snow protects the seedling from the fierce winds and bitter cold that grip the summits. Snow is such an excellent insulator, in fact, that temperatures beneath the crust may be fifty degrees or more above those at the surface. Thus, where air temperatures remain well below zero for weeks on end—and they often do at timber line—a blanket of snow may mean the difference between life and death.

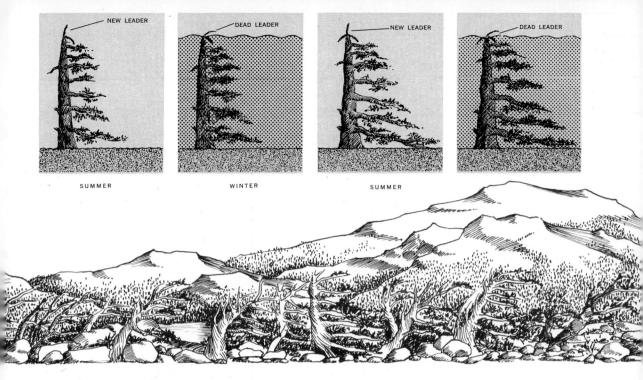

SUMMER　　　WINTER　　　SUMMER

Each summer the tree grows a bit taller, and each winter the snow protects it. Finally it becomes so tall that the tender growing tip, or *leader*, projects above the snowbank that covers the rest of the tree. Bitter cold and the drying effects of constant winds combine to kill the exposed tip.

During the next growing season, another shoot takes over as leader and stretches up beyond the surrounding shoots. But in winter, if it projects above the snow, this shoot also will die. Year after year, the tree sends out new leaders, and year after year they meet the same fate. Examine any of these trees, and you will find a cluster of brown dead twigs at its tip, mute testimony to the severity of living conditions.

Although the tree's upward growth has been halted, however, branches on the leeward side of the trunk continue to elongate. The weight of winter snows may press them down, but the branches keep spreading across the rocky surfaces. Exploring fingers of growth also push up through every crevice in the rocks, for there they find a bit of extra protection from the elements.

Timber line extends a bit farther up the mountains in sheltered ravines, and generally lies at a slightly higher elevation on southern slopes than on cold, north-facing slopes. Thus, timber line is not a rigid boundary that encircles the peak at any particular altitude. It is an uneven zone of transition, a ragged battle line that reflects even the slightest variations in living conditions.

The view from the top

Once you pass beyond the fringe of stunted pines and spruces that mark timber line, trees no longer block your view of your surroundings. Breathtaking vistas of jagged mountain peaks and vast lowlands spread out in every direction around the San Francisco Peaks. The panorama and the feeling of accomplishment that comes with climbing to the windswept summit are rewards in themselves for the long journey to the top of any mountain. You certainly will want to linger on the peak and savor the experience of viewing your surroundings from this strange new vantage point. But you will also want to pause long enough to examine things closer at hand.

At first glance, the uppermost slopes of the San Francisco Peaks seem rather barren. The rock-strewn meadows appear to support little more than short, wiry grasses and sedges. But look more closely and you will find that a variety of life flourishes even here, though many of the plants and animals will be unfamiliar to anyone who has never ventured beyond the temperate lowlands.

Once you pass timber line, you enter a truly frigid climate. Like the vast treeless areas of the Far North, characterized by long winters and low average annual temperatures, the landscape here is genuine *tundra*. Since it is situated at the top of a mountain, it is called *alpine tundra*, but living conditions are much the same as those typical of true *arctic tundra*.

As you might expect, most of the plants that live here grow in arctic regions and at the tops of high mountains in Europe, Asia, Canada, and Alaska as well. Like timber-line trees, most of the mountaintop wild flowers are low, dense, and compact in form. None sends up tall stems that might be buffeted by the never-ending winds. But if you seek out the crevices and sheltered hollows among the rocks, you will find plants with colorful flowers growing in every available pocket of soil.

One of the most conspicuous plants on the San Francisco

Alpine avens is well suited to life at the top: its leaves are small, leathery, and rolled in at the edges. These adaptations help retard the loss of water from the leaves to the relentless drying winds.

Living conditions above timber line are harsh throughout the year: these delicate alpine forget-me-nots have just been battered by pellets of ice during a summer hailstorm. Like many tundra plants, they grow in low, compact clumps that minimize their exposure to the elements.

53

summits is Ross's, or alpine, avens. Dense ground-hugging mats of avens, covered with bright yellow flowers, seem to grow almost everywhere. Another common plant is sticky polemonium, also known as sky pilot and Jacob's-ladder. Clusters of handsome purple-blue blossoms make the polemonium obvious from a distance, but you will recognize it even without the flowers: if you accidentally step on the plant, its crushed leaves give off a powerful and surprisingly long-lasting odor of skunk.

Field chickweed, studded with tiny white starlike flowers, also is likely to be growing nearby, along with several kinds of saxifrage. The word *saxifrage* literally means "rock breaker," and these characteristic mountain plants do indeed seem to be breaking the rocks; they grow best in narrow soil-filled cracks in rocky outcroppings. Dense mats of greenery that may be visible even from afar, on the other hand, may prove to be sibbaldia. This handsome low-growing member of the rose family bears delicate yellow blossoms and three-part leaves that look much like strawberry leaves.

One of the most pleasing features of the alpine gardens is the fact that many species bloom throughout the summer. Plants on the lower slopes begin to blossom as soon as the snow has melted. As the season advances and the snowbanks recede up the slopes, the same species continue to bloom at

Capable of growing at altitudes as high as twelve thousand feet, sticky polemonium may be found in sheltered crevices among the rocks on the very summits of the San Francisco Peaks. Like the related scarlet gilia of the lower slopes, its foliage emits a disagreeable odor when crushed.

A bighorn lamb braces itself against a gust that swirls across a high-altitude mountain meadow. In summer, the sure-footed bighorns are frequent visitors to the summits, where they find good grazing and easy escape from pursuing predators.

successively higher elevations. Plants on lower slopes may already have set seed by the time the same species blossoms at higher altitudes.

In sheltered places, snowdrifts may linger and temporarily delay blossoming. But as sunlight and warmth penetrate the drifts, plants hidden beneath the snow respond to the impending thaw. Frequently they send up shoots with buds that are ready to open before the snow has completely disappeared. One day the ground is blanketed with snow, and the next day it is bright with flowers.

Animals of the summit

Despite the beauty of the alpine gardens and the grandeur of the scenery, you will probably have the feeling that something is lacking. The picture seems somehow incomplete, for there are no animals, or so it seems.

True, a few flies and other insects are humming from blos-

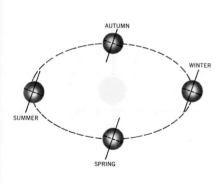

AUTUMN

WINTER

SUMMER

SPRING

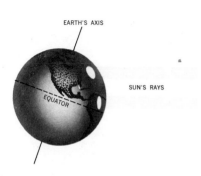

EARTH'S AXIS

SUN'S RAYS

EQUATOR

The cooling of climates between equator and poles results from curvature of the earth's surface. Near the equator, sunlight strikes the earth vertically and its heat is concentrated. In polar regions, sunlight strikes the earth at an angle and its heat is spread over larger areas. Since the earth's axis is tilted, however, the area receiving the most intense radiation varies with the seasons: it is slightly north of the equator in summer and south of the equator in winter.

som to blossom as they search for pollen and nectar. Now and then a water pipit flies overhead or walks purposefully through the grass. Black bears occasionally venture upslope from the spruce-pine forest to hunt for insects and other morsels, and bighorns also visit the treeless summits to graze on grasses and other plants.

But aside from a few voles and other rodents that live in burrows and in crevices among the rocks, there are almost no permanent residents on the mountaintop. Most of the animals you will see here are strictly visitors that venture up to the heights only during the brief months of summer. In winter they remain on the lower slopes, where living conditions are less severe.

Why the San Franciscos?

Climbing to the summit of a mountain is an experience to savor, and anyone who makes it to the top will want to linger for a while before beginning the long descent. Now, while you rest and enjoy the view, is a good time to consider a question that may have been puzzling you, and rightfully so. Why, with all the mountains in the West to choose from, were you encouraged to begin your explorations in the San Franciscos?

Many of the western mountains are higher than the San Francisco Peaks. Some of them are cloaked with glaciers and permanent snowfields. Many have far greater populations of big-game animals and more extensive alpine gardens. Have you made a poor choice? It is a good question, and it deserves an answer.

Perhaps some satisfactory reasons for beginning with the San Francisco Peaks have already been suggested, and others will occur to you. For one thing, no other high mountains in the United States are nearer to the Mexican border and yet include so many alpine and subalpine forms of life. The great saguaro desert may seem remote, yet it is only a few hours' drive from the cool aspen glades you visited near the summits. Many prime features of North American scenery are nearby, and the San Francisco country is significant in the prehistoric and historic life of highly cultured and skilled American Indians.

Yet there is an even more compelling reason for selecting the San Franciscos as an introduction to American moun-

56

tains: these beautiful peaks played a unique role in the history of ecological exploration.

In 1889, twenty-three years before Arizona became a state, the United States Department of Agriculture began a systematic study of the mountains and surrounding territory. During several summers, C. Hart Merriam and a team of expert field scientists catalogued all the forms of life to be encountered from the Arizona desert to the arctic-alpine summits of the peaks. The results of their research, published in a series of famous reports, broadened the concepts of biology and revolutionized prevailing ideas about the distribution of plants and animals. On the basis of their observations, Merriam and his associates proposed and explained a series of *life zones* for the classification of all living things on our continent.

These zones were based on temperature changes from tropical to polar lands. Average annual temperatures become progressively lower as you move from the equator to the North Pole, and living things respond to these gradual changes in climate. They are arranged in a series of more or less parallel bands of forms that are less heat-tolerant with increased distance north from the equator.

We say more or less parallel because, as Merriam noted, a change in altitude has the same effect on living things as a change in latitude: the higher you climb on a mountain, the lower average annual temperatures become. Thus, in warm river valleys, at low elevations, and on slopes exposed to bright sunlight, southern species extend their ranges northward in gentle arcs or fingerlike projections. Northern species extend their ranges southward along mountain chains where living conditions resemble those of more northerly latitudes. Where northern and southern species meet and intermingle there is a zone of transition. North of the transition zone and at higher altitudes are the cold zones, which extend beyond timber line to arctic conditions. South of the transition zone and at lower elevations, the warm zones gradually approach tropical conditions.

Merriam's system of life zones took on even greater meaning for him and his associates because six of the seven zones he proposed are neatly telescoped on the slopes of the San Franciscos and in their immediate surroundings. It is for this reason that we began our mountain explorations on these peaks. Here, if you travel by automobile, it is possible to visit all six of these life zones in a single summer day.

Like polar regions, mountaintops are cold, but for an entirely different reason. Everywhere on earth, heat from the sun is absorbed by surface materials and then reradiated into space. Near sea level the dense atmosphere acts as an insulating blanket, with dust and water vapor impeding heat loss. But in the thinner, clearer air on mountaintops, heat escapes rapidly back into space. As a result, the average temperature drops about three degrees for every thousand-foot gain in altitude.

The seven zones of life

The southernmost life zone in Merriam's system, and the only one not included in the San Francisco area, is the *tropical zone*. It is found in areas near the equator, where frost seldom or never occurs. The tropical zone enters the continental United States only at the southern tip of Florida, where warm waters of the Gulf Stream moderate the climate. Although this zone does not occur in any mountainous areas of the United States, the bases of certain Mexican peaks, such as Orizaba, stand in the true tropics while their summits are always covered with snow.

Slightly to the north or at higher elevations is the *lower austral zone*. (*Austral* is derived from a Latin word meaning "south wind.") This warm but not entirely frost-free zone extends in an irregular band across the southern United States, pushing northward along the seacoasts, in desert regions, and in broad, low-lying river valleys. Recognizing that moisture also is critical in determining the distribution of living things, Merriam and his followers divided this zone into a warm, humid eastern portion, the *austroriparian zone*, and an arid western portion, the *lower Sonoran zone*, which takes its name from the arid Mexican state of Sonora. In the East, the lower austral is the zone of live-oak and pine forests, while in the West it is characterized by saguaro cactuses. It was here, as you will recall, that we began our climb to the San Francisco Peaks.

The next life zone, the *upper austral*, includes much of interior North America. Although it is slightly cooler and moister than the lower austral zone, exact boundaries between the two are difficult to pinpoint. In the West, this is the area of pinyon pines and junipers, and is known as the *upper Sonoran zone*. In the more humid East, this region is called the *Carolinian zone*.

On the basis of temperature changes resulting from increasing elevation, C. Hart Merriam described a series of seven life zones in the San Francisco Peaks area, with each zone characterized by distinctive plant and animal populations. The warmest one, the tropical zone, does not occur in the southwestern United States, but all the others can be observed within a day's drive across Arizona.

TROPICAL ZONE

LOWER AUSTRAL ZONE

UPPER AUSTRAL ZONE

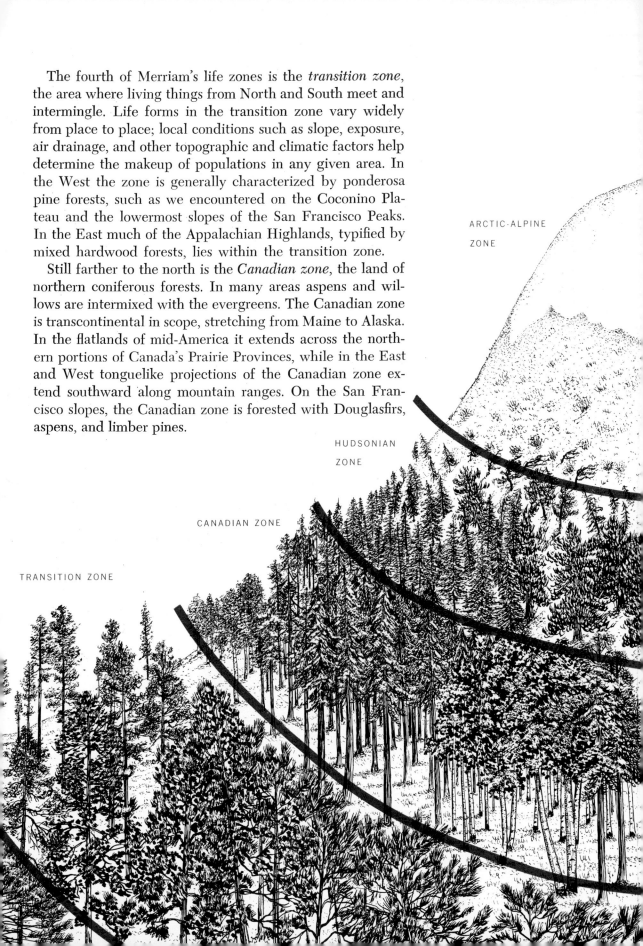

The fourth of Merriam's life zones is the *transition zone*, the area where living things from North and South meet and intermingle. Life forms in the transition zone vary widely from place to place; local conditions such as slope, exposure, air drainage, and other topographic and climatic factors help determine the makeup of populations in any given area. In the West the zone is generally characterized by ponderosa pine forests, such as we encountered on the Coconino Plateau and the lowermost slopes of the San Francisco Peaks. In the East much of the Appalachian Highlands, typified by mixed hardwood forests, lies within the transition zone.

Still farther to the north is the *Canadian zone*, the land of northern coniferous forests. In many areas aspens and willows are intermixed with the evergreens. The Canadian zone is transcontinental in scope, stretching from Maine to Alaska. In the flatlands of mid-America it extends across the northern portions of Canada's Prairie Provinces, while in the East and West tonguelike projections of the Canadian zone extend southward along mountain ranges. On the San Francisco slopes, the Canadian zone is forested with Douglasfirs, aspens, and limber pines.

ARCTIC-ALPINE ZONE

HUDSONIAN ZONE

CANADIAN ZONE

TRANSITION ZONE

The *Hudsonian zone*, named for the forested lowlands around Hudson Bay, is another transcontinental zone that extends south along high mountain chains. The dominant trees are dwarfed spruces, firs, and pines and low-growing willows, birches, and aspens. The upper or northern margin of this zone is clearly defined by timber line. In the San Franciscos, as on many western mountains, the Hudsonian zone is typically forested with Engelmann spruce and foxtail pine.

The northernmost zone in this system of classification, the *arctic-alpine zone*, includes all the cold, treeless areas encircling the North Pole and extending southward on high mountain peaks. In the West, isolated outposts of the arctic-alpine zone occur on high mountaintops well into Latin America. In the East, alpine tundra extends south only to the higher peaks of the Adirondack Mountains in northern New York.

Thus moving from a warm climate to a cold one, or from the equator to the North Pole, Merriam's life zones are: the tropical zone; the lower austral zone, including the austroriparian and lower Sonoran zones; the upper austral zone, including the Carolinian and upper Sonoran zones; the transition zone; the Canadian zone; the Hudsonian zone; and the arctic-alpine zone.

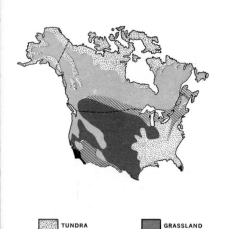

TUNDRA   GRASSLAND

CONIFEROUS FOREST   DESERT

MIXED FOREST   TROPICAL FOREST

DECIDUOUS FOREST   CHAPARRAL

Although many ecologists still find Merriam's system of life zones useful and meaningful, especially in mountain country, others prefer to classify land areas in terms of larger, more inclusive units known as biomes. Approximate areas of major biomes in North America are shown here.

The trouble with Merriam's system

The system of life zones proposed by Merriam and his co-workers had an immediate and far-reaching impact on the scientific world. Field biologists everywhere accepted the system and wrote books and lengthy articles in which they attempted to assign all living things to their appropriate life zones. Before long, however, it became clear that a zonation system based strictly on temperature could not account for all occurrences of living things. Too many other factors, such as soil, wind, and exposure, certainly play a role in determining the kinds and numbers of plants and animals to be found in any given area.

In an attempt to overcome these objections, Merriam and his followers gradually modified their system. But they still failed to meet the criticisms of many ecologists, particularly those from the flatter midsections of America. Throughout the prairies and plains, changes in vegetation from south to north are gradual, and far more difficult to observe than on

60

an abrupt mountain slope. Life zones simply do not and cannot serve to explain and classify the distribution of plants and animals in level lands. As a result, Merriam's system of life zones has lost most of its former acceptance.

Most ecologists have adopted the concept of *biomes*, much broader ecological units that include all the plants and animals characteristically found living together in an area. Thus, areas of North America now are generally described in terms of much more inclusive ecological units such as coniferous forest, deciduous forest, desert, tundra, and grassland.

Even so, Merriam's system has not been completely abandoned. Life zones, so clearly defined and strongly marked as to catch an observer's eye, continue to be useful in any area of rapidly changing elevations. Wherever you travel in the mountains, east or west, north or south, you are bound to notice zonation according to altitude. Your understanding of the life around you will be richer and more meaningful if you interpret it in terms of such a system.

The upside-down mountain

By way of contrast, you can, if you wish, see some of Merriam's life zones illustrated in a dramatic fashion at another of northern Arizona's great scenic areas. From the San Francisco summits, if the air is clear, you will see a great shadow on the landscape some eighty miles to the north. This huge irregular scar across the face of the earth is the Grand Canyon of the Colorado River.

The Indians, so we are told, have a name for the Grand Canyon which means something like "mountain upside down." Assuming that the translation is accurate, the name is both imaginative and exactly true to life. This enormous hole in the earth is indeed a mountain in reverse, and a very large one at that. Most eastern peaks, if they could somehow be transplanted to river level, would be entirely hidden below the canyon's rim, for the chasm in many places is over a mile deep.

As you leave the San Francisco Peaks and head north across the Coconino Plateau, you pass once again through the pinyon-juniper forest of the upper Sonoran zone. At the South Rim of the canyon you climb just enough to return to the transition zone. Here, overlooking the spectacle of the

Just as changing elevations on mountains result in an orderly zonation of living things at different altitudes, the abrupt slopes of the Grand Canyon are characterized by distinctive vegetation zones.

ZONATION IN THE
GRAND CANYON

ALTITUDE
IN FEET

9000

8000

7000

6000

5000

4000

3000

2000

CANADIAN ZONE   UPPER SONORAN ZONE

TRANSITION ZONE   LOWER SONORAN ZONE

61

canyon itself, you will find ponderosa pines and many of the same birds and flowers that greeted you as you emerged from Oak Creek Canyon.

But what about life within the Grand Canyon? There are no highways to carry you down to river level, some five thousand feet below. If you want to investigate the plants and animals of the depths, you will have to make the rugged descent to the bottom on foot or by mule train. Either way, the trip is tiring, but well worth the effort.

Life is sparse along the canyon walls, but you will detect patches of greenery on the infrequent ledges and plateaus on the way down. When you pause to investigate, it will come as no surprise to discover that they are the familiar pinyon pines and junipers of the upper Sonoran zone. The most conspicuous animals on the way down will be lizards: collared lizards, chuckwallas, and flat, spine-studded horned lizards.

The farther you descend into the canyon, the hotter it becomes. At the beginning of your descent from the South Rim, the thermometer may have stood at a comfortable 80 degrees; by the time you reach river level, temperatures are likely to have soared to 100 or even 105 degrees. You have not traveled far in terms of horizontal distance, but in terms of life zones your descent is equivalent to a giant step toward the tropics. At river level you are once again in the lower Sonoran zone. The giant saguaros are missing, but mesquite, yuccas, cholla cactuses, and many other plants that you saw in the desert flourish at the canyon bottom.

A last look at the San Franciscos

Before leaving the Grand Canyon area, you will want to make one final excursion, this time to the canyon's North Rim. The North Rim's Kaibab Plateau stands one to two thousand feet higher than the South Rim, a gain in elevation that is sufficient to return you to the Canadian zone. Here

Cactuses and other typical desert plants flourish in the depths of the Grand Canyon. If you were to climb the canyon walls, you would observe transitions in vegetation strikingly similar to those that marked your approach to the San Francisco Peaks, for the Grand Canyon is indeed "a mountain upside down."

you are surrounded by a magnificent forest of Douglasfir and aspen, interspersed with open grassy areas where wild flowers bloom profusely. Mule deer, mountain lions, Kaibab squirrels, and a wealth of other animals flourish on the plateau.

As you travel through this beautiful forest and explore its many attractions, you will discover occasional side roads, narrow and dusty perhaps, but inviting to anyone who enjoys visiting relatively undisturbed countryside. One of the finest of these roads leads west to Point Sublime, where a parking area overlooks a matchless vista of the Grand Canyon. Far below the canyon's rim, you see the shimmering streak that marks the course of the Colorado River and a world that is astonishingly different from the Douglasfir forest surrounding the overlook—a few miles away in space, perhaps, but in biological fact a journey from Mexico to Canada.

And as you stand on the rim, overwhelmed by the panorama, you raise your eyes. There, breaking the horizon to the south, are the San Francisco Peaks. They are your mountains now, for you have visited them. You are still within their keeping; the kachinas still are looking down on you.

A scenic overlook on the North Rim of the Grand Canyon provides a matchless vantage point for viewing two great spectacles of northern Arizona: the canyon itself, gouged a mile deep into the plateau, and, eighty miles away, the San Francisco Peaks, towering a mile above it. Although physical opposites, both offer priceless opportunities for learning more about the life of mountains.

Ancient Mountains

All the mountains of western North America are young as geologists count time. The forces that raise up high peaks and build long mountain chains have operated relatively recently along the Pacific Coast, as compared with those in the East. Even now, in California and to the north, the earth's crust shudders occasionally under the stresses of earthquakes, and a number of volcanoes still are active in Alaska. Lassen Peak, a volcano in California, last erupted in 1922 and may still be active, while the most recent great earthquake to rock the Alaska coast occurred in 1964.

All the eastern mountains, on the other hand, are ancient. Most of the great mountain chains of the eastern United States and Canada were elevated during the geological era known as the Paleozoic, about 300 million years ago, long before the more advanced forms of life such as birds and mammals had appeared on the earth. A few of the eastern mountain ranges are even older. Rocks in New York's Hudson Highlands and in Virginia's Shenandoah National Park, for example, are estimated to be about 1.1 billion years old.

BIRTH OF A MOUNTAIN

DOMING

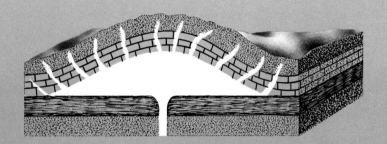

Dome mountains form when molten material from the earth's interior rises through a fissure in the earth's crust. Instead of escaping on the surface, the molten material spreads between subterranean rock layers and causes the surface rocks to rise like an enormous blister. The Henry Mountains in Utah are excellent examples of dome mountains.

FOLDING

Folded mountains, such as the Appalachians, are created when internal stresses in the earth's crust push sideways against rock layers, causing them to rise upward in the form of gigantic folds or wrinkles. Upheavals of this sort, termed "revolutions," usually require millions of years for completion.

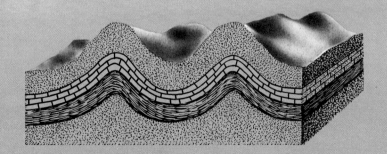

FAULTING

Fault-block mountains, such as the Sierra Nevadas and the Grand Tetons, form where enormous blocks of rock slip upward in relation to the surrounding terrain along great cracks, or faults, in the earth's crust. Each time the rocks slip slightly along the fault, the land for miles around shudders with an earthquake.

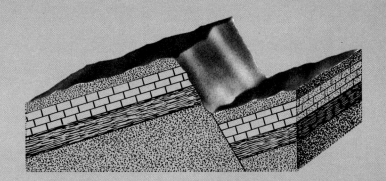

VOLCANISM

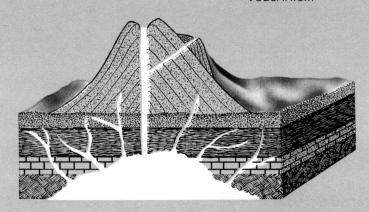

Volcanic mountains, such as Mount Rainier and other peaks in the Cascade Range, are accumulations of debris that build up where material from the earth's interior escapes through vents or fissures in the earth's crust. Each time the volcano erupts, additional deposits of ashes, rocks, and molten material, or lava, accumulate on the mountain's slopes.

A closer look at eastern mountains

The two major systems in the East are the Appalachians and the Laurentian Highlands. The Appalachian Mountain system—actually a loosely related group of much smaller ranges—begins in western Newfoundland, crosses Quebec's Gaspé Peninsula, and continues southwest to Georgia and Alabama. A few of the better known ranges in the Appalachian chain are the Notre Dames in Quebec, the White Mountains in New Hampshire, the Green Mountains in Vermont, the Alleghenies, the long Blue Ridge system, and the Cumberlands of Kentucky and Tennessee.

The Laurentian Highlands lie mostly in Canada, stretching from Labrador to Hudson Bay. They enter the United States in only two areas: in New York, where they form the Adirondacks, and around the western end of Lake Superior, where they form a series of hills and low mountains in Michigan, Wisconsin, and Minnesota.

Time has mellowed all the eastern mountains. Because of

The graph below shows dramatically the differences in elevation between western and eastern mountains in North America. Most of the western mountains are relatively young, and the forces of erosion have had little time to wear them down. Eastern mountains are much older; although many of them may once have stood as high as the mountains of the West, today none of them even approaches the elevations of their western counterparts.

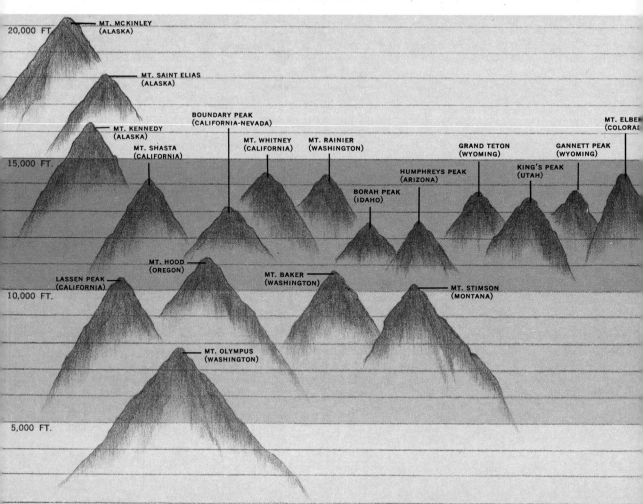

20,000 FT. — MT. McKINLEY (ALASKA)

— MT. SAINT ELIAS (ALASKA)

BOUNDARY PEAK (CALIFORNIA-NEVADA)

MT. ELBER (COLORAD

— MT. KENNEDY (ALASKA)

MT. SHASTA (CALIFORNIA)

MT. WHITNEY (CALIFORNIA)

MT. RAINIER (WASHINGTON)

GRAND TETON (WYOMING)

GANNETT PEAK (WYOMING)

15,000 FT.

HUMPHREYS PEAK (ARIZONA)

KING'S PEAK (UTAH)

BORAH PEAK (IDAHO)

MT. HOOD (OREGON)

LASSEN PEAK (CALIFORNIA)

MT. BAKER (WASHINGTON)

MT. STIMSON (MONTANA)

10,000 FT.

— MT. OLYMPUS (WASHINGTON)

5,000 FT.

their great age, they generally lack the sharp peaks, abrupt cliffs, and angular lines that characterize most western ranges; their contours have been softened and their valleys broadened by the erosive powers of streams and, in northern areas, by sheets of glacial ice. In the distant past, many of the eastern ranges may have stood as high as the Rockies, but today the eastern summits are modest in elevation, more often hills than true mountains.

None of the eastern peaks, for example, is as high as the Kaibab Plateau, which stands eight to nine thousand feet above sea level. The tallest peak in the Adirondacks is only a little over a mile high. A few of the Appalachian summits in New Hampshire, North Carolina, and Tennessee exceed six thousand feet, but the majority are lower. In addition, most of the eastern mountains are arranged in long ridges; their highest points stand only a little above the surrounding peaks. A few, such as Mount Katahdin in Maine, soar three thousand feet or more above the surrounding plateau, but they are definitely exceptions.

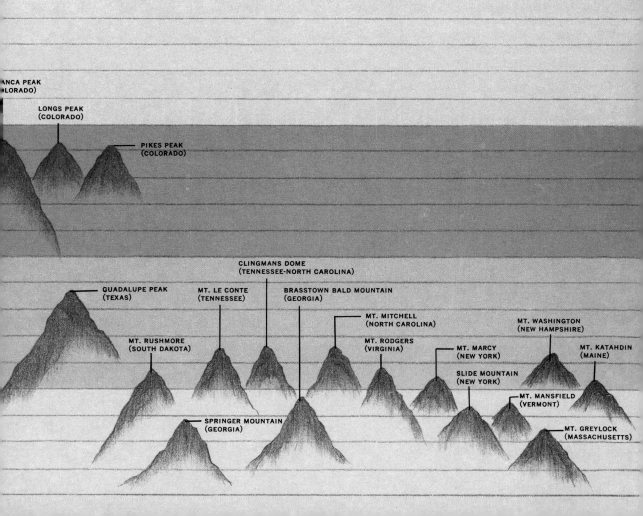

What makes them special

Clearly, then, the mountains of the East and West cannot be judged by the same standards. Western mountains are majestic, so tall and massive that they inspire awe and, perhaps, even terror in the beholder. Most of the eastern peaks are too gentle and too inviting to provoke such reactions. And possibly they are too familiar. About half the people in North America live within a day's drive of the Appalachians or the Laurentians; those who live nearby are sometimes tempted to take their mountains for granted, to accept them as familiar features holding little that is exciting or glamorous.

Yet many of the eastern peaks are impressive in their own modest way. No one who has ever looked from Pinkham Notch to the summit of Mount Washington in New Hampshire or caught a glimpse of Mount Marcy from Lake Placid in New York is likely to forget these sights. Anyone who knows only the evergreen forests of the West is certain to be impressed by his first view of an eastern mountain covered with oaks, hickories, birches, maples, tuliptrees, and other deciduous trees, especially if he sees them in their

Autumn-burnished oak leaves contribute to the tapestry of color that blankets the eastern mountains every fall. With scores of species of broadleaf trees, each taking on distinctive colors, the East's autumn spectacle is unsurpassed anywhere in the world.

Springtime in the eastern mountains is marked by the flowering of dozens of different kinds of trees and shrubs. One of the most beautiful is mountain laurel, whose delicate blossoms seem as fragile as fine porcelain.

splendid autumn foliage. And the East's springtime spectacle of blossoming redbuds, dogwoods, rhododendrons, mountain laurel, and azaleas has no western counterpart.

Thus, though mountains on the Atlantic side of the continent may not match those of the West in size, they have their own special attractions and can be inspiring in their own way. In order to get a closer look at the eastern ranges and the plants and animals that live among them, we shall pay special attention to two peaks: Mount Marcy in New York as a representative of the Laurentians and Mount Le Conte in Tennessee as a typical Appalachian peak.

New York's finest

The Adirondacks, which are thought to be the mere eroded roots of a much taller range of ancient mountains, fill much of northern New York State. Just west of Lake Champlain on the New York–Vermont border, their granite summits rise abruptly from the lowlands. Here the Adirondacks reach

73

Is mountain wilderness worth preserving? The people of New York think so, for in that state —and within a day's driving distance of 35 million Americans—lies a 2.2-million-acre tract of Adirondack woodlands which the state's constitution decrees "shall be forever kept as wild forest lands." Although villages dot the Adirondack Forest Preserve and private summer homes fringe many of the lakes, the vast expanses of forest lands themselves remain relatively undisturbed by man. Stay at a public campsite beside a pleasant Adirondack lake or find lodging in one of the shelters built along the hundreds of miles of trails that thread among the mountains, and you will have an opportunity to enjoy unspoiled mountain wilderness at its best.

The adaptable red fox, which ranges across most of North America, is equally at home in mountain forests, on open farmlands, and even about the fringes of suburban areas. This pup, one of a litter of three to nine young, was born in late spring; by autumn it will be ready to strike out on its own.

their greatest elevations, with several summits towering a mile or more above sea level. Farther south and to the west the mountains gradually become lower and less rugged in their contours. At Thousand Islands myriads of miniature peaks project from the water of the St. Lawrence River, forming a bridge that links the Adirondacks with Canada's geologically similar Laurentian Highlands.

Covered almost entirely by dense, mature forests, the Adirondacks are a gentle wilderness, but a wilderness nevertheless. More than 2,200,000 acres of this vast mountain tract have been set aside by the people of New York as the Adirondack Forest Preserve, and the state's constitution declares that this great park shall remain "forever wild."

The result is one of the finest outdoor recreation areas in the East. Hundreds of hiking trails thread through the wilderness, and pleasant camping areas border many of the

76

White-tailed deer, one of the major resources of the Adirondack wilderness, attract thousands of hunters to the area every autumn. In the hard days of winter, scores of deer congregate in sheltered valleys. If hunters have been unsuccessful in reducing the herds to numbers that their winter range can support, many of the deer die of starvation.

innumerable glacier-carved lakes and ponds that dot the mountain valleys. Deer, bears, raccoons, minks, and other creatures roam through the forests. Beavers, once trapped almost to extinction, are becoming abundant once again in many areas. Otters, martens, and fishers, though rare, still are seen occasionally. Every summer, visitors by the thousands flock to the area for fishing, boating, hiking, and camping, and in fall and winter they come to enjoy the Adirondacks' big-game hunting and the famous ski slopes and bobsled runs.

New York's Adirondack Forest Preserve, in short, is a complete recreation area with attractions for everyone. And over it all there hovers the elusive spirit of the North Country—the scent of pine and fir, the songs of the hermit thrush and winter wren, and the delicate beauty of white birches fringing the margins of a thousand lakes and streams.

Lake Tear-of-the-Clouds, the placid Adirondack pond where the Hudson River begins its journey to the Atlantic Ocean, mirrors the rocky summit of Mount Marcy, the highest point in New York State. Rising 5344 feet above sea level, Mount Marcy's crest is one of the few peaks in the East that extend beyond timber line.

To the top of Mount Marcy

An ideal starting point for an exploration of the Adirondacks is Mount Marcy. With its crest 5344 feet above the Atlantic, Marcy's summit is the highest point in New York. Although its base lies in the transition zone, the last five hundred feet of its peak extend into the arctic-alpine zone, forming a tiny outpost for boreal life hundreds of miles south of true arctic regions.

In this sense Mount Marcy is a member of a select company, for very few eastern mountains extend beyond timber line. Marcy and nearby Mount McIntyre are the only ones in the Adirondacks that do. Mount Washington and several others in New Hampshire's Presidential Range, plus Mount Katahdin in Maine, complete the list in the northeastern United States. Several peaks in the Appalachians are higher than most of these, but they lie so far to the south that their summits do not reach arctic-alpine conditions.

Another advantage of selecting Mount Marcy as an introduction to northeastern mountains is the fact that no roads lead to its summit. The mountain has been relatively unaltered by human activities. The lack of highways means that you must travel on foot, but this is no real hardship, for foot travel is the best way to get the feel of mountain country. Since there are a number of inviting trails to the top, you can take your choice of routes. All of them involve several hours of climbing, yet none is so difficult as to require the use of special mountaineering techniques.

The most convenient starting point is the village of Keene Valley near the base of the mountain. Several trails begin here, and if you feel you need a guide (or simply someone to help carry your camping gear), professional woodsmen are available in the village. Should you decide to go it alone, you need not fear getting lost; all the trails are plainly marked.

One of the most attractive routes is the trail that travels up the mountain beside John Brook. The trail is only about ten miles long, but it climbs steadily upward to several thousand feet in altitude. In places it is steep and fairly rough, just difficult enough to keep things interesting but easy enough for beginners to manage.

Remember that there are no convenient inns or lodging places along the way. You will be able to eat only the food you carry with you, and your shelter at night will have to

A vacation at a secluded campsite is an ideal way to discover the true personality of the Adirondacks. Nearly one thousand miles of well-marked trails lead visitors to remote valleys and mountain crests that lie far beyond the sights and sounds of civilization.

come out of your pack. After dark, you will be glad if you thought to bring along an extra blanket; nights are cool on Marcy, even in summer. If you should find the summit cloaked in mist and freezing rain—a distinct possibility at any time of year—you will be relieved to know that a snug, secure rock shelter has been built near timber line.

Let thrushes lead the way

Anyone who has an appreciative knowledge of birdsong probably will use the notes of thrushes to chart his progress up Mount Marcy. Throughout the Northeast, the woodlands are inhabited by a group of brown-backed, spotted-breasted thrushes that includes some of America's most notable songsters. Although no single thrush species will be found all the way from Keene Valley to the top of Mount Marcy, thrushes of one sort or another will be with you until you reach timber line.

Wood thrushes are the first species you will encounter. These familiar birds, with reddish heads and dark, distinct polka dots on their creamy breasts, often nest in groves in city parks and suburban areas. But they are most at home in forests like the one at the beginning of the John Brook trail, where the slopes are covered by an attractive mixture of birches, beeches, and maples. This is typical transition-zone forest throughout the East. These so-called northern hardwoods extend all the way south to Georgia, and wherever they occur, you are likely to find wood thrushes. As you hike along the lower portions of the trail near Keene Valley, you will soon become familiar with their distinctive flutelike calls.

Curiously, you will quickly learn to recognize their nests as well. Wood thrushes usually build in shrubs and on the lower branches of trees within five or ten feet of the ground. They characteristically incorporate several withered beech or other leaves in the foundations of their nests. But if careless hikers have dropped bits of tissue or scraps of paper along the trail, the birds are likely to substitute these conspicuous markers for the usual foundation of leaves.

A bit farther up the trail, pines and hemlocks become more frequent in the forest. Here, where cool, moist air

In ascending Mount Marcy, an experienced naturalist can gauge his approximate altitude by using his ears: each level has its characteristic species of thrush. These wood thrushes— the involuntary foster parents of a brood of cowbirds—are common only on the lowest Adirondack slopes.

from the summit pours down the ravine created by John Brook, the transition zone is giving way to the Canadian zone. This borderline forest is the best place to look and listen for veeries, or Wilson's thrushes, although they also venture down into the hardwoods. Veeries, the least spotted of the spotted-breasted thrushes, are a good deal more withdrawn and less easily observed than wood thrushes. But since they seem to prefer to nest near water, your hike along this portion of John Brook will be brightened by the sound of their slurred, descending notes piping from the treetops.

While veeries seem to hover on the borderline between the transition and Canadian zones, the next two species you encounter are definitely Canadian. Several miles from its beginning, the trail to Marcy angles away from the tumbling waters of John Brook and enters a mixed forest of spruces, hemlocks, birches, and mountain ashes. By this time both wood thrushes and veeries have disappeared. The forest echoes instead with the songs of the hermit thrush and the Swainson's, or olive-backed, thrush. Both, it might be noted, are also abundant in the Canadian-zone fir-aspen forests on the San Franciscos.

The rather dull gray-brown Swainson's thrushes often are among the most common birds in mixed coniferous forests. In contrast to the descending musical scale of the veeries' song, the melodious notes of Swainson's thrushes rise in pitch toward the end of their song. If your campsite is near a brushy opening in the forest, you are almost certain to hear Swainson's thrushes singing from the treetops in the dim light both at dawn and in the evening.

Hermit thrushes also tend to seek high perches, usually on the uppermost twig of a coniferous tree, and fill the darkening woods at evening with ringing melodies. During the day you are likely to glimpse only their reddish tails as they slip into dark tangles of shrubs. They also lurk in dense stands of black and white spruces and in fragrant, low-growing balsams. Superficially, the hermit's song resembles that of the wood thrush. Each series of rising notes begins on a slightly higher pitch than the preceding one, however,

Shafts of morning sunlight soon will dissipate the mist that veils a rocky Adirondack stream. Watercourses such as this are particularly good places for observing birds and other mountain wildlife, especially just after dawn and just before nightfall, when many forest animals come to the stream for a drink.

and pauses between the phrases are longer than those in the wood thrush's song. The total effect is so hauntingly beautiful that many outdoorsmen rank the hermit thrush as the most gifted of all our native songbirds.

The last of the thrushes you will see on Marcy's slopes are the gray-cheeked thrushes. Although they are difficult to distinguish from Swainson's thrushes, their song is distinctive, a curious blending of the notes of both the veery and Swainson's thrush. Their notes are on a descending scale at first, but rise in pitch toward the end of the song.

The gray-cheeked thrushes are prominent only on the windswept slopes above four thousand feet, where they inhabit the Hudsonian-zone forest of flagged and stunted spruces and firs. Of all our spotted-breasted thrushes, these are the most boreal, and Mount Marcy is one of the southernmost limits of their breeding range.

Thus, in their own musical way, the brown-backed thrushes provide a kind of summary of the life-zone system in the Adirondacks. Wood thrushes, neither strictly northern nor entirely southern, flourish in the transition zone, while veeries are most at home where the transition zone is merging with the Canadian zone. Hermit and Swainson's thrushes,

The hiker who reaches the top of Mount Marcy is rewarded with a view of gently rolling peaks that spread out for miles in all directions. Although seemingly barren, the rocky summit is dotted with a rich variety of alpine wild flowers.

in contrast, are strictly Canadian; they live only in the spruce forests here and on high mountain ridges to the south. Gray-cheeked thrushes dwell in the low coniferous forests of the Hudsonian zone. When you hear them on Mount Marcy, you will be comforted by the knowledge that you are nearing the end of the climb.

The end of the trail

Timber line on Marcy is like timber line everywhere. The kinds of trees may vary in different areas, but the general appearance of this pioneering forest is the same in both the East and West. On Mount Marcy, the timber-line trees are low balsam firs and red spruces, yet their growth forms are nearly identical to those of the Engelmann spruces and fox-tail pines that grow about the summits of the San Franciscos. The trees are characterized by the same nearly prostrate trunks, spreading branches, and adventuring twigs that creep through every sheltered crevice.

Just a short distance below tree line, the forest is alive with birds—gray-cheeked thrushes, blackpoll warblers, win-

ter wrens, and an occasional pair of three-toed woodpeckers. But the birds are effectively contained by timber line. The only ones to be seen on Marcy's alpine tundra are slate-colored juncos and a few white-throated sparrows.

Resident mammals also are extremely scarce on the summit. Here, as on most of the eastern peaks that rise above timber line, insects are the only animals that are at all abundant. If the sun is shining and temperatures are genial, you will find swarms of insects stirring among the rocks and hovering over the snowbanks that linger in sheltered places well into June. There are flies, a good variety of butterflies, and many kinds of beetles and other insects. Some, such as the butterflies, may be carried to the heights by strong rising winds, while the scarcity of birds and other predators may account for the abundance of flies and some of the others.

Wherever you find insects, you are almost certain to find flowers as well, and Marcy's summit is no exception. Everywhere that the snow has melted, the ground is covered with bright carpets of color that will help you forget aching muscles and blistered feet. A good many of the flowers are familiar mountain species, such as bluets, tiny violets, and

A clump of diapensia finds shelter in a niche among the lichen-covered rocks above timber line. Like many alpine plants, this dwarf evergreen is common both in arctic lowlands and on high mountain peaks at more southerly latitudes.

In common with many other alpine plants, Lapland rosebay has tiny, tough leaves that resist drying and a sprawling growth habit that helps it escape the extremes of weather. The closely related rhododendrons of lower altitudes, in contrast, have leaves up to nine inches long and sometimes grow thirty-five feet tall.

dwarf buttercups. In addition, Marcy's peak provides sanctuary for a number of arctic plants whose ranges do not extend so far southwest as the San Francisco Peaks.

One of these is diapensia, a true mountaineer that would be just as much at home in Labrador, in Norway, or on Asiatic summits. In June it is studded with white bell-shaped flowers, but its dense, ground-hugging mats of evergreen leaves are attractive even after the blossoms fade. One of its most notable companion plants is the miniature rhododendron known as Lapland rosebay, another plant that is widely distributed throughout arctic regions. In June, this little evergreen shrub is covered with surprisingly large and handsome roselike blossoms.

Another of Marcy's arctic-alpine plants is black crowberry, a shrub that thrives on rocky coasts in the North and on exposed mountain peaks in more southerly areas. In autumn these dwarf evergreens are covered with black berrylike fruits. On the coast of Labrador and other northern shores, the berries are a primary food source for golden plovers and other shore birds about to embark on migration flights to

The vinelike bearberry willow
of the alpine tundra bears
little resemblance to its
hundred-foot-tall relatives of the
lowlands, yet its pink catkins
proclaim it to be a true willow.

winter quarters thousands of miles to the south. Crowberries, in fact, probably are critically important to these birds. They seem to be a major source of the thick layers of fat that sustain the birds during their long flights to the south.

Strangely enough, a few woody plants that we normally think of strictly as trees also are able to grow beyond timber line. In arctic lands, certain willows and birches venture out on the tundra, and are perhaps the most northern "trees" in the world. But they are dwarfed forms that creep almost like vines across the ground. One of these, bearberry willow, is abundant toward Marcy's summit, where it hugs the rocks and creeps through narrow crevices. Despite their small size, the "trees" bear typical willow catkins which are visited by tiny insects in search of pollen. A miniature forest of this sort may seem strange and rather unreal, but it is the only kind of forest you can expect to find on Marcy's summit.

South to the Appalachians

The Laurentian Highlands come to an end on the southern slopes of the Adirondacks; all other eastern mountains are part of the Appalachians. Yet the differences between the two systems are largely matters of topography and geological history. In terms of the life they support, the northern Appalachians and the Laurentians are nearly indistinguishable. Most, if not all, of the plants and animals found in the Adirondacks also occur in the Green and White Mountains of Vermont and New Hampshire. Forests are essentially the same on the slopes of Mount Marcy, Mount Washington, and Mount Katahdin, and all of them support similar birds, identical mammals, and most of the same insects.

Differences between northern and southern mountains, on the other hand, are substantial and highly significant. As you travel south from Mount Marcy to the mile-high peaks of southern Appalachia, you will observe a great many changes in the makeup of plant and animal populations. Many of the typically northern species gradually drop out

A moose browses in the shallows of a quiet pond at the base of Mount Katahdin, a 5268-foot-tall granite mass that forms one of the most imposing peaks in the northern Appalachians. Like Mount Marcy, Katahdin is one of the handful of eastern mountains whose summits rise above timber line.

Weller's salamander is an example of an endemic species, a plant or animal restricted to a limited geographic area. This handsome little amphibian occurs only in high mountain forests of extreme northeastern Tennessee and nearby areas of Virginia and North Carolina.

of the picture and are replaced by hardy forms from more southerly latitudes. More important, the southern Appalachians harbor many species of plants and animals that are *endemic*: they are peculiar to this area, occurring here and nowhere else unless they have been transplanted. This situation is of such great biological significance that it requires a bit of further explanation.

For one thing, the Appalachians are a land mass of tremendous age. In all the hundreds of millions of years since their formation, they have stood well above sea level. From time to time, arms of the ocean invaded the valleys of the Mississippi and a hundred lesser rivers, but through it all the towering Appalachians stood high and dry. Their crests and ridges have been eroded, lowered, and transformed, but never since their formation have the Appalachians been submerged beneath the sea.

Thus, the southern Appalachians represent one of nature's oldest experiment stations. Here the long, slow process of evolution has continued almost without interruption for hundreds of millions of years. Land and fresh-water plants and animals that were exterminated elsewhere continued to live and evolve into new forms in this great natural laboratory. One large and important group of salamanders —the plethodons, or lungless salamanders—for example, are

90

believed to have originated in the southern Appalachians.

Equally important in its effects on plant and animal life was the age of glaciers—the Pleistocene epoch, in the terminology of geologists. As recently as ten or twenty thousand years ago, much of the Northeast was covered by tremendous sheets of glacial ice. As these colossal masses of ice swept down from the North, however, they were partially halted by the Appalachians. In extreme southwestern New York, where the mountains begin to reach substantial heights, the glaciers divided in two, sending tongues of ice southward into New Jersey to the east and into Ohio to the west. But most of central Pennsylvania and the mountains to the south were spared from the crushing burden of ice, for they were simply too high and too far south to be engulfed by the glaciers.

As a result, sudden and conspicuous changes in plant and animal life are evident south of the glaciated areas. In the North nearly all forms of life were exterminated by the glaciers. But as the ice sheets inched slowly across the land, many northern plants and animals extended their ranges to the south and found a place of sanctuary in Appalachian valleys. When the glaciers finally retreated and the climate grew warm again, some of the plants and animals gradually reinvaded northern areas. But others found appropriate living conditions simply by extending their ranges up mountainsides, and there they have survived until the present. Moreover, as we shall see in greater detail in the next chapter, some of the forms that became isolated on mountaintops have since evolved into new species.

Thus, south of the glaciated areas, there is a sudden increase in the number of different kinds of reptiles and amphibians, some of which represent true endemic species. In addition, many of the southern herbs and woody plants are species that once grew much farther north but since the ice age have been unable to reinvade formerly glaciated areas. Before the age of glaciers Appalachian slopes, both northern and southern, were covered by great forests that included many trees now known only as fossils in the North. Yet this forest persists to the present in the southern Appalachians, reaching its best development in fertile, well-watered valleys at the bases of high ridges.

If we are to understand and appreciate the southern highlands, the significance of all these things can scarcely be overstated. While half the continent was submerged be-

■ GLACIATED AREA

In the portion of the United States covered by glacial ice during the most recent ice age (*shaded area*), many forms of life were exterminated, but others found refuge by extending their ranges to the south. Since many of these have not yet reinvaded the North, areas south of the line of maximum glacial advance harbor a greater variety of plants and animals than do areas to the north.

Mists that swirl almost daily about their lofty summits are responsible for the name of the Great Smoky Mountains, where sixteen peaks exceed six thousand feet in altitude. Heavy rainfall on the mountains nurtures the growth of lush vegetation and tall trees.

neath the sea or inundated by ice, the southern Appalachians stood alone as a land mass. For millions of years they have served both as a sanctuary for plants and animals that were exterminated elsewhere and as a natural laboratory where new forms of life have gradually evolved from the old.

On the slopes of Mount Le Conte

One of the best places for studying the life of the southern Appalachians is in Great Smoky Mountains National Park, a unique preserve of beautiful parkland straddling the Tennessee–North Carolina border. The mountains, which take their name from the banks of mist and haze that frequently swirl about their summits, epitomize the tranquil charm of the southern highlands.

Mount Le Conte, the peak that will serve as our introduction to the Great Smokies, looks down on Gatlinburg,

Tennessee, where the park's headquarters are located. Although we tend to think of eastern peaks as small, Mount Le Conte is impressive in terms of the only meaningful standard for measuring the grandeur of a mountain: from base to summit, it rises from about 1500 to 6593 feet above sea level. Put another way, the distance from bottom to top is nearly equal to the rise from Flagstaff to the summits of the San Franciscos.

As was true of Mount Marcy, no highways lead to the top of Mount Le Conte. The view from the summit is a treat reserved for those who make the ascent on foot or by horseback. You can shorten the hike by driving to a nearby parking lot on the highway that crosses the park. In this way you gain so much in elevation that you will have a much easier climb to the three peaks that form Le Conte's crest. As a further convenience to travelers, Mount Le Conte, unlike Marcy, has overnight accommodations at the top.

But the best way to get to know Mount Le Conte is to

make the entire climb on foot, preferably from the park headquarters area near Gatlinburg. The ascent will be even more interesting if you keep in mind the system of life zones that mountains display so well. Along the way you will encounter many old friends from below timber line on Mount Marcy, as well as a number of plants and animals that you saw on the lower slopes of the San Franciscos. Once again you will realize that Merriam gave us a useful concept for explaining life in steep country.

A land where North meets South

On the lowest slopes of Mount Le Conte, in the area around park headquarters, plants and animals are definitely southern. The land is forested with a mixture of pines and hardwoods, and some of the common birds are Carolina wrens, cardinals, and Kentucky warblers, none of which is likely to be found around the base of Mount Marcy.

Before you gain very much in elevation, however, you enter the transition zone, that ecologically challenging and often puzzling meeting place of northern and southern forms of life. Much of the Great Smokies, in fact, lies in the transition zone. The whole vast territory from the lowlands nearly to the summits of the highest peaks is one great melting pot, with unexpected associations of living things.

The park includes over a hundred different kinds of trees, as many as are to be found growing naturally in so limited an area almost anywhere in the world. The dominant tree in the transition-zone forests is the sugar maple, which grows just as vigorously in northern Vermont and even Canada. But here it seldom grows in pure stands. Side by side with the sugar maples, beeches, and yellow birches—trees that are dominant in the Adirondacks—there may be such southern specialties as Carolina silver-bell trees and yellowwoods. The silver bells range northward to Virginia, but to the north they tend to be rather small and shrubby; they are at their best in the Smokies, often growing seventy or eighty feet tall. In early spring, just before the leaves come

The familiar cardinal of suburban lawns is one of more than two hundred species of birds found in Great Smoky Mountains National Park. The area also boasts fifty species of mammals and about thirteen hundred different kinds of trees, shrubs, and herbs.

SILVER-BELL TREE

YELLOWWOOD

out, each twig is adorned with dangling white bell-shaped blossoms, each one an inch or so long. In many places the silver bells are so common that their blossoms cloak entire slopes with a haze of white.

Yellowwoods, on the other hand, are among the park's genuine rarities. They, too, have white flowers, but the pea-like blossoms are borne in large clusters near the tips of the twigs. The yellowwoods are unpredictable, for they do not bloom every year, and blossoming time varies from season to season. Fortunately, the park naturalists can usually tell you if any are blooming in the area.

But suppose you have found your yellowwoods and admired these southern prizes. As you continue to hike around the bend, the trail angles down into a ravine beside a clear, swift stream. The air grows cool and moist, and hardwoods disappear from the forest cover. Suddenly you are transported far to the north, for you find yourself surrounded by a pure stand of Canada hemlocks, towering forest giants whose massive trunks rise straight up for a hundred feet or more. Little red squirrels, dwellers in coniferous forests almost everywhere, chatter noisily from the treetops, enjoying the abundant supply of seeds in the hemlock cones. Yet just over the ridge you may spot an eastern fox squirrel—a large, dark southern relative of the common gray squirrel—whose range in the Appalachians extends no farther north than Pennsylvania.

There can be no doubt that this is the transition zone. It may be a bit confusing at first, but you soon will get used to the idea of hearing Canada warblers and those famous southern mimics, yellow-breasted chats, calling from the margins of the same forest clearings. These unexpected associations of living things are the very essence of the transition zone. And they are among the greatest attractions of the Smokies: these lovely mountains harbor one of the world's most fascinating mixtures of plants and animals from half a continent.

Three peaks at the top

As you approach the three small peaks that together compose Le Conte's summit, the forest gradually takes on a distinctly northern aspect. You are still in Tennessee, but you have entered a southward extension of the Canadian-

96

Among the most abundant and characteristic of southern Appalachian shrubs, rhododendrons often grow in dense, impenetrable thickets known locally as "slicks." The large, clustered blossoms range from white through various shades of pink and purple.

zone spruce-fir forest. Instead of white or black spruce and northern balsam fir, the trees are red spruce and Fraser balsam fir. Yet, superficially at least, the forest closely resembles the transcontinental Canadian zone found much farther north.

The trees are similar, and so are many of the plants on the forest floor. Canada Mayflower, wood oxalis, alder-leaved viburnum, and other familiar northern shrubs and wild flowers add variety to the coniferous forest. Many of the birds also are just what you might expect to find. Juncos, winter wrens, brown creepers, red-breasted nuthatches, and black-throated blue warblers are common here in summer, just as they would be in New Brunswick or parts of Ontario.

Yet there are curious, unexpected differences. On northern mountains, no rhododendrons grow in the Canadian zone; near the top of Le Conte, as on all other peaks in the southern highlands, rhododendrons grow in dense stands,

The flying squirrel does not fly at all, but is an accomplished glider; with the help of the winglike membranes that connect its front and hind legs, it can soar for one hundred feet or more. Since this little rodent is primarily nocturnal, few people have ever seen one in the wild.

often of two or more species. An attractive relative of diapensia, the evergreen white-flowered galax, also is an abundant and characteristic ground cover.

Another plant, sand myrtle, is so common about the summit that Myrtle Peak, one of the three on Mount Le Conte's crown, was named for it. This dwarf evergreen heath has tiny oval leaves and bears clusters of showy white flowers accented by long reddish stamens. But the most interesting thing about sand myrtle is its curious distribution. It grows in only two places: on southern Appalachian peaks and on sandy pine land along the Atlantic coastal plain.

A number of other plants share this strange pattern—mountaintop species that are also found on the coastal plain but are not known from any of the territory in between. Presumably the plants originally were restricted to mountaintops, where they were preserved through long periods of inundation and glaciation. Later, as opportunities arose, the plants apparently spread downward along stream courses and became established in congenial habitats in the lowlands. Even so, it comes as a surprise to discover a high, sandy Appalachian ridge covered with a plant that you first came to know on Long Island, Cape Cod, or Cape May.

Like the plants, the animals of Le Conte's summit present a few surprises. The true Canadian zone has very few salamanders, yet southern mountaintops are alive with salamanders of many kinds. More species probably are found in the Smokies than in any comparable area in the world. On the other hand, many characteristic Canadian-zone mammals, such as porcupines, fishers, and martens, are missing, although red-backed mice, least weasels, northern flying squirrels, and rock voles are found in the Smokies as well as in more northerly regions.

Thus, life on Mount Le Conte and its neighboring peaks is quite different from the life on Mount Marcy. Here you will observe the layering of living things that is characteristic of all mountain slopes. But, because of location, climate, and geological history, things are a bit mixed up. The Smokies lie mostly in the transition zone, yet even their Canadian zone displays a curious overlapping of ranges and life forms. All in all, these mountains add up to a fascinating mixture of living things, one that amazes and delights thousands of visitors every year.

Although the red-backed mouse spends most of its time on the forest floor, it occasionally explores the lower branches of trees and shrubs as it forages for seeds, nuts, bark, and insects. This shy, five- to six-inch-long rodent is active both night and day.

An ecological riddle

Climbing just one peak provides barely an introduction to the Great Smokies. The park and nearby mountains include a great many other attractions, all of them intriguing and a few that are downright puzzling.

Take *balds*, for example. You may have heard of these curious treeless areas at high elevations in the southern highlands, and perhaps you would like to visit one. The most accessible is Andrews Bald, near the center of the park. You can reach it by driving to the Forney Ridge parking area near Clingmans Dome. From the parking area, a well-marked trail leads directly to the bald just two miles away.

Andrews Bald looks much like any other forest clearing, here and there growing up in shrubs and low trees, but for the most part covered by grasses and herbs. It may not seem very exciting, until you ask a question: why is the bald here at all? It isn't anywhere near tree line: none of the southern Appalachian peaks is tall enough to reach timber line. Forests flourish both above the bald and below it. And since it apparently has been here for a long time, why doesn't

In May and June, rhododendron blossoms add bold splashes of color to many southern Appalachian "balds." So far, no one has found a satisfactory explanation for the presence of these grassy or shrub-covered openings in the otherwise unbroken mountain forests.

the area grow up in forests like those that cover the adjacent slopes? These are good questions, and a lot of people have tried to find the answers, but so far without success.

More than eighty of these grassy openings are scattered through the Appalachians from Virginia south to Georgia. Most of them stand at least four thousand feet above sea level, and a few are a good deal higher in the mountains. Some people contend that the balds are simply clearings made by early settlers who grazed their cattle on these heights. The balds certainly have been used as pastures, but if we can believe pioneer stories, balds already existed on the mountains when the first settlers arrived.

Others have speculated that the clearings were made long ago by Indians who sought these high places to look at the rising sun and worship their Great Spirit. Maybe so, but Indians have not been active here for a long time, yet trees do not seem to be reclaiming most of the open areas.

Still others have suggested that the balds resulted from attacks by insects that live only under certain conditions of temperature and moisture. But this explanation does not seem satisfactory either, for many slopes with similar climates do not have balds at all. And one more question: why are balds found in the southern Appalachians, but not in the long ranges to the north? The most likely answer to this ecological riddle is that no single explanation can account for the origin and persistence of each and every one of these curious grassy openings.

Whatever the reasons for their formation, balds are interesting places to visit. If you arrive at Andrews Bald at just the right time, you may surprise a wild turkey catching grasshoppers, feeding on berries, or dusting itself on a patch of bare earth. Very few deer live in the virgin forests of the Smokies, but the few that are present gather near the margins of balds to feed on legumes and succulent herbs.

Andrews Bald is also a good vantage point for watching the flight of ravens. These oversized crows look somewhat like their smaller relatives, but they have heavier bills, fan-shaped tails, and voices that sound quite different from those of other crows. Alternately soaring and then flapping their wings, these noisy scavengers often patrol roads just at treetop level in an endless search for food. Their courtship antics are especially amusing to observe, during their mating flights the big black ravens often turn complete somersaults in the air.

Though now uncommon over much of its former range, the wild turkey still is seen from time to time about the edges of balds in the Great Smoky Mountains.

101

The strikingly beautiful flame azalea (*left*), one of the
smaller species of rhododendron, occurs in warm hues
that range from lemon-yellow to deep brick-red.

In addition to grasses, many of the balds are partially
grown up in flowering shrubs. The handsomest by far is
flame azalea, one of the finest ornamental shrubs to be found
in the East. In spring the azaleas bear large clusters of
trumpet-shaped flowers with long, gracefully curved stamens
protruding from each bloom. No two plants have flowers
that are quite identical; the blossoms vary from the palest
of yellows to rich orange-reds. When they bloom, the azaleas
frequently dot the balds and mountainsides with crazy quilts
of flamelike hues.

Rhododendrons also are so common on many of the southern balds that they sometimes cover the openings with
dense, tangled evergreen thickets. Such distinctive areas
have their own special name or, rather, names: ecologists
refer to them as *heath balds*, and local people call them
laurel slicks. Whatever you choose to call them, they are
one of the park's most popular floral attractions. In June,
when the rhododendrons are in bloom, the heath balds
provide a spectacle that rivals the attractions of many a
botanical garden.

In the valley of the big trees

Once you have seen a grass bald, you will also want to visit
another Appalachian ecological specialty, a *cove*. You have
already passed through one, Sugarlands Cove, when you
started to climb from park headquarters to Mount Le Conte.
Although it is smaller and less famous than Cades Cove to
the south, Sugarlands Cove is well worth investigating.

Coves are found at the bases of steep slopes where tempestuous mountain streams are constantly carrying down
eroded soil and decaying organic material. Where the slope
becomes less steep, the stream fans out, begins to flow less

Rushing streams like this one deposit thick beds of soil
and organic material in sheltered coves at the bases of
the Great Smoky Mountains. Because of their deep,
fertile, well-watered soils, the coves support amazingly
lush growths of trees, shrubs, and wild flowers.

Throughout its range, the bobcat is relentlessly persecuted by humans, yet it still holds its own in the Great Smokies and other wilderness areas. Hunting mostly by night, it preys on rabbits, hares, and all sorts of rodents.

rapidly, and deposits its debris in the form of a delta. The result is an accumulation of deep, rich soil, well watered by the rushing mountain stream that created it. Westerners will notice the similarities between cove deposits and the *fan deltas* that form at the mouths of canyons in arid mountain country.

Because of their fertile soil and dependable water supply, coves are famous for the big trees they produce. The largest known examples of a good many kinds of trees have been discovered in Appalachian coves. Even more impressive is the tremendous variety of species making up the stands. It is not at all uncommon to find forty or fifty different kinds of trees in a single cove. This is not a usual situation, for in most forests two or three species normally dominate the stand.

Sugarlands Cove takes its name from the many sugar maples growing there, but the maples share the cove with dozens of other species. Black cherry and black walnut, two of the finest of American furniture woods, thrive here and in other Appalachian coves. So do the valuable white oak; white ash, which is especially sought after for baseball bats; the light but strong and enduring tuliptree; and such other prized species as birch, basswood, magnolia, buckeye, mulberry, and many more. A good many of the trees and shrubs, moreover, bear showy blossoms. The springtime display of flowering dogwoods, redbuds, magnolias, silver bells, tuliptrees, yellowwoods, locusts, and dozens of other species is truly a sight to behold. Although this wealth of flowering trees is characteristic of forests throughout the southern highlands, it is never more spectacular than in a fertile, well-watered cove.

At one time the cove forests also included the American chestnut, a tree whose abundant crops of nuts were eaten by almost every kind of game animal. But now the chestnut has practically disappeared from Appalachian forests. Chestnut blight, a bark disease accidentally introduced from Asia around 1900, has all but exterminated these legendary forest giants. In many places, however, the chestnut roots still send up new shoots, and now and then a tree grows large enough to produce nuts. As a result, researchers continue to comb the forests in the hope that they will find a few blight-resistant trees.

Routes north and south

Even when you have visited all these places, you will not have exhausted the possibilities of the Great Smokies. Certainly you will want to climb to the top of Clingmans Dome, the highest point in the park and the second highest peak in the East. Standing 6642 feet above sea level, Clingmans Dome is only forty-two feet lower than North Carolina's Mount Mitchell. The easiest way to climb Clingmans Dome is to drive to the parking lot at Forney Ridge and then walk the half-mile trail to the summit. You may be surprised when you discover the ultramodern observation tower on the mountaintop, but you will be glad it is there; the balsams are so dense at the top of Clingmans Dome that, without some sort of lookout tower, you would miss the splendid view from the summit.

If you enjoy hiking, the long miles of the Appalachian Trail will be an irresistible temptation. This most famous of American walkways cuts across the center of the park,

The American chestnut—once widespread in the East, but now almost extinct—bears long, slender clusters of white blossoms in early spring. Its small edible nuts, which are encased in bristle-studded burrs, at one time provided a major source of food for squirrels and other animals.

AMERICAN CHESTNUT

BLOSSOMS

NUT

more or less following the border of the two states that meet here. One moment you are in Tennessee, the next moment in North Carolina.

In all, the trail extends about two thousand miles north and south, following the backbone of the Appalachians from Springer Mountain, Georgia, to Mount Katahdin in Maine. And nowhere is the trail so difficult that special mountaineering skills are required. Anyone who can hike at all can explore the Appalachians on this great walkway, camping overnight in the log shelters that have been built at convenient intervals along the way. With a knapsack on his back and the spirit of adventure in his heart, anyone can set out for an afternoon, a weekend, or an entire summer on the Appalachian Trail, one of the most imaginative recreation developments in the world.

If your time and energy are limited, you can explore the nearby Appalachians by car. Extending north from the

The famous Appalachian Trail, which threads its way from Maine to northern Georgia, offers hikers and campers a unique opportunity for enjoying the best of the eastern mountains. First proposed in 1921, the last section of the 2050-mile-long trail was completed in 1947. This group of campers is exploring the trail in the White Mountains of New Hampshire.

Smokies is the Blue Ridge Parkway, an extraordinary mountain highway that connects the Great Smokies with Shenandoah National Park, some 470 miles away. Even this does not tell the whole story, however, for at Shenandoah the Blue Ridge Parkway connects with Skyline Drive, which continues still another hundred miles northward to Front Royal, Virginia.

Throughout their entire length these two scenic highways follow the crests and ridges of the central Appalachian Mountains, dipping up and down from one to six thousand feet above sea level. And all along the way they are bordered by forests, wild-flower gardens, and scenic overlooks that provide spectacular vistas of the surrounding countryside.

Either way—on foot or by car—these routes north and south through the Appalachians offer unsurpassed opportunities for getting to know mountain country.

The lure of the mountains

Eastern mountains, then, are different—not so rugged and remote, nor quite so picturesque and romantic as the western peaks, but with their own special charms for all that. The West may boast a colorful atmosphere of cowboys and Indians, of covered wagons and the hardships of the trail, but eastern mountains have a history too: they breathe the spirit of Daniel Boone, of the riflemen who fought at Kings Mountain, and of settlers who struggled across the highlands on the Wilderness Road. Western traditions center on buffalo and longhorn cattle; the East has its black bears and wild turkeys, both legendary creatures in their own right.

Though perhaps a bit tame by comparison with the giant ranges of the West, eastern mountains cast a quiet spell all their own. There is always something more to be seen just over the ridge, and in the East the path across the ridge is open and inviting. Come with an open mind and keen senses, and here, too, you will find excitement. Open your eyes and you will discover adventure along the trail as you learn to adapt your ways to the demands of a country of hills and forests.

The alpine tundra of New Hampshire's Mount Washington is embroidered with a mixture of lichens, Lapland rosebay, and alpine azalea. Although less rugged than their western counterparts, the mountains of the East nevertheless have a quiet charm which, once experienced, will lure you back again and again.

Islands
in the Sky

Islands in the sky—that is precisely what they are, these peaks that soar so high above their surroundings. Like islands in the sea, mountains have their own populations of living things, plants and animals that can survive only under the special set of living conditions imposed by high elevations. All true mountain species, moreover, find their appropriate environments only at certain elevations on the slopes. Within a given life zone they flourish; above it or below it they cannot long survive.

A famous example will demonstrate how this situation came about. In the White Mountains of New Hampshire, the Appalachian Trail remains above tree line for almost twenty miles as it winds around the peaks and across the gaps that separate Mount Adams, Mount Jefferson, Mount Washington, and other nearby summits. In its entire 2000-mile length, this is the longest stretch of the trail above timber line. As you hike this section of the trail in summer, almost anywhere along the way you can expect to find a few medium-sized pale brown butterflies with unspotted wings. The females are most likely to be hovering about weeds and grasses, where they lay their eggs.

These inconspicuous, seemingly insignificant little insects, known as the White Mountain butterflies, are rather famous in the annals of biology. They are found only in this area of the White Mountains, where they are restricted to the bleak summits that project like islands from the surrounding sea of conifers. The butterflies do not descend into the forests on the lower slopes because they cannot; despite fierce winds and bitter cold, only the alpine tundra on the mountaintops provides the living conditions that they seem to require for survival.

White Mountain butterflies have close relatives in polar lands around the globe, and a colony of similar butterflies lives on the treeless summit of Mount Katahdin in Maine. But the White Mountains are the most southerly outpost in North America for any butterflies of this group. How did they come to exist on these isolated peaks so far removed from the principal home of their kind?

How the butterflies found the mountaintops

Some educated guesswork is necessary if we are to account for the curious distribution of these insects, but all the evidence seems to point to glaciers as the most logical explanation for their presence in the White Mountains. During the ice age, just yesterday as geologists reckon time, tremendous glaciers almost overwhelmed the Northeast. Because of a slight cooling of world climates, more snow fell in winter than could melt under the summer sun. As the snow piled up in the North, it gradually changed to ice; vast arms of the ice began to push southward from the subarctic centers of accumulation.

The glaciers advanced slowly across the land, however; just in front of the ice sheets, the climate undoubtedly remained mild enough to allow the survival of many arctic forms of life. Around the ice sheets that still exist in the Canadian Rockies and in Greenland, for example, plants grow right up to the margins of the ice. In places where the

The leading edge of an alpine glacier inches its way down a mountain slope, slowly crushing a thicket of alders standing in its path. Although they seem large, the glaciers of today are but puny reminders of the mile-thick ice sheets that blanketed much of North America, Europe, and Asia as recently as twelve thousand years ago.

Sightseers' automobiles *(right foreground)* are dwarfed by Athabasca Glacier in Jasper National Park in the Canadian Rockies. Glaciers form where winter snow accumulates faster than it can melt in summer. Compressed into ice by their own weight, the masses of ice creep slowly downslope at rates varying from half an inch to one hundred feet per day. Like most of today's glaciers, Athabasca is receding: its leading edge is melting more rapidly than the glacier is moving forward. The piles of rocky debris, or "moraines," in the foreground were deposited when the glacier penetrated farther into the valley than it does today.

ice thins and melts, flowers bloom and a few insects remain active within the very shadows of the glacial walls.

Eventually the ancient glaciers advanced far enough to cover all of New England—all, that is, except for a few isolated mountaintops that protruded above the ice. The glaciers may have been five thousand feet or more in thickness, but they were not quite high enough to overwhelm Mount Washington and the neighboring peaks.

Even in glacial times the climate must have been warm enough for some growth of green plants and some animal activity on the mountaintops, just as there is life around existing glaciers. Thus, as the butterflies of the Far North moved southward in front of the advancing ice, they found sanctuary on these tiny outposts of tundra that projected from the sea of ice. And there they have survived until the present, an enduring souvenir of the age of glaciers.

Gifts of the glaciers

As we explored the mountains of the East and West, we observed many similar reminders of the Pleistocene epoch. Lapland rosebay, diapensia, and the other circumpolar plants that grow above tree line on Mount Marcy presumably also were forced southward by the advancing ice sheets. When the glaciers receded and the climate warmed again, some of the plants followed the ice fronts northward and reoccupied their former homes on the arctic tundra. But others found congenial living conditions simply by moving up mountainsides. There they have remained, marooned on islands in the sky ever since the final retreat of the glaciers.

Even mountain trout streams, in a sense, are a gift of the

When the continental glaciers retreated at the end of the last ice age, the climate gradually warmed and vegetation zones on mountains changed accordingly. As temperatures rose, plants requiring a cool climate were forced to extend their ranges to the north in order to survive. . . .

SOUTH   NORTH   SOUTH   NORTH

glaciers, for without the help of glaciers, trout would never have found their way to streams in the southern mountains.

Trout are members of the salmon family, a group of relatively primitive fish that are widely distributed throughout the Northern Hemisphere. All the available evidence suggests that the family probably originated in the Arctic. To many members of the family, glaciers posed no real problem. Atlantic salmon and several species that live along the Pacific Coast are adapted to spend most of their lives in the sea, and return to fresh water only to spawn. As glaciers advanced across the land and northern rivers became icebound, the salmon simply shifted their spawning areas to the south.

Most trout, on the other hand, cannot survive in salt water. They thrive only in cool, rapidly flowing inland streams. When the ice sheets began to form, the trout undoubtedly moved southward in front of the glacial walls and probably even benefited from the increase in cold, tempestuous streams that flowed out from the glaciers.

In North America, as we have seen, the advancing glaciers divided and flowed around the sides of major mountain masses. As trout were forced southward, they found their way into the cold, dependable streams that continued to rush down the mountainsides, and they gradually extended their range as they discovered interconnections between the streams.

Since the western mountain ranges are high, wide, and nearly continuous, they provided vast areas for trout to colonize. As a result, western mountains were invaded by several kinds of trout—rainbow, cutthroat, and others. But in the East only one species, the eastern brook trout, found its way into the streams draining the much less extensive

. . . But in many areas, they found appropriate living conditions simply by moving to higher elevations. In the mountain area shown here, coniferous forests (*black*) gradually moved higher on the mountains and were replaced at lower elevations by deciduous forests. Tundra areas in turn grew smaller, until they all but disappeared in southern areas.

SOUTH   NORTH   SOUTH   NORTH

Many characteristically northern plants, including buck bean *(top)* and large cranberry *(bottom)*, thrive in cool, boggy upland valleys in the southern Appalachians, where living conditions are strikingly similar to those found in watery Canadian muskegs. Unexpected combinations of plant and animal species make these mountain bogs especially intriguing to ecologists.

mountain systems. Even so, brook trout did manage to extend their range throughout Appalachia, all the way south to the mountain streams of western Georgia.

Of course the picture has been greatly complicated in the past hundred years or so, as men learned to raise trout in hatcheries and introduce them to waters where they are not native. The success of such efforts only demonstrates the adaptability of these hardy fish and their ability to thrive in suitable streams, if only they are given the opportunity. As a result of human tampering with the natural scheme of things, millions of western rainbow trout now inhabit eastern streams, while eastern brook trout flourish in Rocky Mountain and Pacific Coast waterways. And both eastern and western streams have been enriched by the importation of brown trout from Europe. The native trout that the first settlers discovered in the clear, rushing brooks of the American mountains, however, first found their way there as a result of the ice age.

Bog islands

Many of the plants and animals forced southward by the advancing ice were unable to compete with similar forms already present in southern lands. They lost out in the struggle to survive and have simply vanished from the face of the earth. But others, more fortunate, found bits of territory suited to their needs and have survived there to the present.

One very important *habitat*, or living place, of this sort is the southern mountain bog. These bogs, just as truly as areas of mountaintop tundra, are islands in the sky, for they also serve as places of refuge. Here, too, isolated populations of typically northern plants and animals are able to survive in areas far removed from the normal range of others of their kind.

Mountain bogs are found in shallow, poorly drained upland valleys that are nearly surrounded by ridges of higher land. Normally the only outlet for excess water is a small stream that flows through an inconspicuous gap in the encircling ridges. Upland bogs of this sort are fairly common in the central Appalachian Highlands. The largest and most characteristic are found in valleys on either side of the Allegheny backbone, a mountain crest that is practically

The tamarack, a characteristic tree of cool, damp areas, ranges across much of northern North America (*shaded area*) but also finds suitable living conditions in a few mountain bogs as far south as West Virginia and western Maryland.

119

continuous from south-central Pennsylvania to southwestern Virginia. Some of the most famous ones are Cranesville Swamp on the West Virginia–Maryland border, Cranberry Glades and Canaan Valley in West Virginia, and Burkes Gardens in Bland County, Virginia. All of them have many plants and animals in common, and all differ strikingly from their surroundings.

Slopes around the bogs generally are forested with a mixture of maple, beech, birch, and other hardwoods typical of these areas. Animals also are just what you might expect to find at these latitudes. But the bogs themselves resemble misplaced islands of Canadian landscape. Many are fringed by stands of balsam fir and tamarack, both trees of the northlands. Another northern tree, red spruce, flourishes in nearly all the bogs, while quaking aspen, largetooth aspen, black ash, and several other broadleaf trees frequently live about the damp margins.

Beneath the trees and in more open areas, the bogs usually are covered by a scattering of shrubs such as Canada yew, chokeberry, serviceberry, shrubby St.-John's-wort, and occasionally bog rosemary. Several kinds of bog orchids spangle the surface with bright blossoms in spring and summer, while cranberries grow heavy with plump red fruits in the fall. Some of the other common plants are goldthread, dwarf dogwood, sundew, and purple-flowered pitcher plant. None

Among the typically northern plants and animals that range south of the Appalachian bogs are the nine-inch-high bunchberry (left)—a close relative of flowering dogwood—which is found as far north as Alaska, and the white-throated sparrow (right), whose breeding range extends northward to Newfoundland.

of them seems particularly remarkable, except for one thing: nearly all these plants are found in bogs in Ontario and northern New England, yet here they are, growing in the general latitude of Washington, D.C.

Animals of the bog present the same sort of story. Water shrews and star-nosed moles live in the bogs, feeding on the wealth of earthworms. Northern flying squirrels and snowshoe hares also are plentiful, yet most of their kind live much farther to the north. White-throated sparrows, among the finest singers of Canadian forests, reach the southern limit of their breeding range in a bog in northern West Virginia. Instead of migrating farther north, common snipe frequently spend the summer at another bog just a few miles away. Cranberry Glades, just a bit farther south, is the southernmost nesting area for such birds as Swainson's and hermit thrushes, Nashville and mourning warblers, northern waterthrushes, and purple finches. A number of other northern birds, including winter wrens, brown creepers, red-breasted nuthatches, and golden-crowned kinglets, also thrive about the mountain bogs.

These water-soaked hollows in the southern mountains, in short, would look distinctly like Canadian-zone forests if it were not for the presence of so many southern birds and mammals. The bogs and their margins support a mixture of species that are not normally found together.

How the bogs became mixing pots

SPHAGNUM MOSS

Sphagnum moss, the most abundant plant in the bogs of southern Appalachia and elsewhere, normally grows in the form of huge mats. Only the top layer is alive; beneath the living plants is a thick mass of decay-resistant dead material that is gradually compressed to form peat.

The explanation for this situation is fairly simple: bogs are surrounded by pockets of cool, moist climate in an otherwise temperate region. Their climate is not related to elevation, however, for the bogs do not stand high enough on the slopes to reach the Canadian zone. Yet the basis for their cool, moist living conditions is not hard to find. The cause lies underfoot.

Open portions of a bog are overgrown with thick mats of pigeon-wheat moss and sphagnum, or peat moss. On the surface the mosses are alive and green, or if it is autumn, the sphagnum may be colored with brilliant shades of orange and red. But if you probe beneath the surface and beyond the reach of sunlight, you will find that the plants are pale and colorless. Deeper still, the delicate rosettes of moss become dark, discolored tangles of partially decayed plants. Most of the mat is a deep accumulation of dead mosses which has built up over thousands of years. In many places the mat is so thick that it springs gently beneath your feet.

Squeeze a handful of the moss and notice the amount of moisture it contains: sphagnum and pigeon-wheat moss both absorb considerable moisture, as much as twenty times their own weight. Though it may have been weeks since the last rain, a steady stream of water will ooze from the sponge-like mass of moss in your hand.

It is all this moisture that explains the cool climate around the bogs. A great deal of heat is lost as water slowly evaporates from the moss, and temperatures remain cool. In addition, the cooler air, which is heavier than warm air, is trapped in the depression around a bog. Thus, throughout the summer, the water-soaked bogs remain so cool that they are, in effect, natural refrigerators, just right for the survival of plants and animals that normally live much farther north.

Again, the inhabitants of the bogs presumably got there as a result of glaciers. When the ice sheets retreated, these isolated populations of northern plants and animals became concentrated in the scattered pockets of cool, moist climate where they were relatively free from competition from more southerly forms. Most were permanently stranded in the bogs.

On the other hand, since the bogs are relatively limited in area, a good many southern forms also spill over from the surrounding slopes and invade the bogs as visitors if not as permanent residents. Thus the southern mountain bogs are mixing pots, supporting unexpected combinations of plants and animals that were forced together by glaciation and have not yet become completely separated.

Where hares abound

One of the more intriguing animals to be found in some of the mountain bogs and elsewhere in the surrounding territory is the snowshoe hare. These big rabbitlike animals inhabit parts of the red-spruce belt in West Virginia, and some spill across the border into the few remaining spruce forests in Virginia. The hares in this area seldom venture much below three thousand feet in elevation, and if there are no stands of red spruce, they will not be found at all. The hares do not eat red spruce—its needles and twigs are almost worthless as food—but they apparently require the shelter provided by dense stands of the tree. Game-management specialists have tried to introduce hares outside the spruce belt, but all such efforts have been unsuccessful.

So far as historical records show, moreover, the West Virginia population of snowshoe hares has been completely isolated from all others of its kind for at least one hundred years. South of this area, there are no hares at all. To the north, the next population of snowshoe hares is found in eastern Pennsylvania, a good two hundred miles away. Thus the West Virginia hares inhabit a genuine island in the sky.

Mountain turncoats

Despite their larger size, snowshoe hares sometimes are called snowshoe rabbits. Actually, rabbits and hares are quite distinctive, especially in details of their life histories. New-born rabbits are naked, blind, and helpless. All hares, in contrast, bear relatively mature young. Hares are covered with fur at birth, their eyes are already open, and within a few hours they are able to move about on their own.

The "snowshoe" part of the name derives from the great size of the hares' hind feet. They serve as highly efficient snowshoes which enable the animals to travel across deep snow without sinking in.

Another adaptation to northern winters accounts for their

Pigeon-wheat moss, which is also known as haircap moss, often grows on the sphagnum mats in Appalachian bogs. It bears male and female reproductive bodies on separate plants. The male bodies are inconspicuous rosettes at the tips of the stems. After fertilization, the female plants bear grainlike spore cases on slender four-inch stalks.

PIGEON-WHEAT MOSS

An animal for two seasons, the snowshoe hare is an inconspicuous brown in summer *(below),* and in winter it wears a coat of pure white *(opposite)* that blends perfectly with the snow. The winter hare is gnawing bark from the trunk of a shrub. Feeding scars are also evident on plants in the summer picture.

other common name, varying hares. In summer their fur is brown or tan, with white only on their underparts, tails, and feet. When cold weather sets in, the brown fur is replaced by a coat of pure white, a camouflage that makes them nearly invisible against winter snows. A number of other northern animals share this remarkable adaptation to changing snow cover, but the snowshoe hare is the only animal of this sort to be found on the isolated mountains of Virginia and West Virginia.

This characteristic, in fact, probably explains the absence of hares on mountains farther south. During the ice age, snowshoe hares very likely extended their range far beyond Virginia and West Virginia, since spruce-fir forests clothe the higher summits all the way down to the Smokies. But now that the climate has grown warmer, the southern peaks

often remain bare of snow for long periods every winter. In such an area, any pure white animals would be so conspicuous that they soon would be eliminated by predators. If any snowshoe hares ever existed in the Smokies, they have long since disappeared. The right foods are available, and spruce forests provide the cover hares require, but the weather simply is not suited to their survival.

Boom and bust for snowshoe hares

Throughout their range snowshoe hares are of special interest to students of *population cycles,* those curious, unexplained ups and downs in abundance that characterize many animal populations. The hares are particularly good examples of this

Records of fur purchases made by Canada's Hudson Bay Company provide a classic illustration of population cycles. For unknown reasons, snowshoe hare populations reach a crest every ten or eleven years and then decline abruptly. Since lynxes prey almost exclusively on the hares, their populations have shown a corresponding fluctuation with variations in the numbers of snowshoe hares.

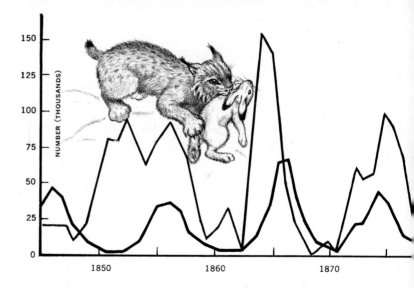

phenomenon, for every ten or eleven years their populations reach a crest, which is followed by a sudden and severe decline in numbers.

The fates of a number of other animals are closely tied to the hares' boom-and-bust population cycles. In far-northern forests, snowshoe hares are the primary prey of many flesh eaters. When the hares increase in abundance, so do the lynxes, foxes, hawks, owls, and other predators that feed on them. But as regularly as clockwork the hares begin to die off, and then the predators fall on hard times. Many die of starvation, and others, desperate for food, fall easy victim to fur trappers. Some, such as goshawks and snowy owls, migrate far south of their normal range in search of food.

Lemmings and a number of other northern animals undergo similar boom-and-bust cycles. The intervals between their population crests and troughs are not in every case the same as the ten- to eleven-year hare cycles, however, nor are their cycles necessarily synchronized with those of other species. The result of all this has been an endless debate among biologists. Different observers seldom agree on the population statistics, time intervals, or causes of the cycles. Some specialists are not even convinced that population cycles actually occur, at least over wide areas.

Some have suggested that animal cycles are caused by periodic occurrences of *sunspots*, cloudy areas on the sun's surface which affect solar radiation. But the only argument offered in support of this theory is the fact that sunspots also happen to become abundant at ten- to eleven-year intervals. As a result, this theory has been abandoned and scientists have sought other, more convincing explanations for population cycles. Some scientists speculate that periodic

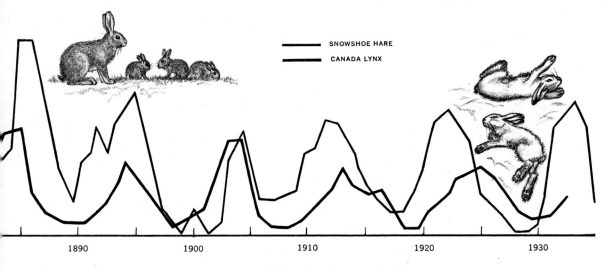

SNOWSHOE HARE
CANADA LYNX

1890   1900   1910   1920   1930

variations in the vitamin content of key foods may hold the answer to animal cycles. Still others have offered a number of different explanations. But whatever the causes, it cannot be denied that many animals, at least in local areas, do indeed experience periodic fluctuations in population.

The point of all this, so far as our story is concerned, is that the snowshoe hares on West Virginia mountains undergo population cycles. Hare populations on several high peaks in east-central West Virginia have been under continuous study for thirty-five years. Through all that time hares have been present on the mountains, but in some years they have been plentiful, in other years nearly absent. At no time did the hares appear to be overcrowded. Food, moreover, has always been abundant, and so starvation has nothing to do with the periodic decline in their numbers.

When these studies were finally completed, the results were compared with data gathered in other areas of the Northeast. Strangely enough, the peaks and troughs in West Virginia hare populations coincided almost exactly with the times of abundance and scarcity in hare populations in New York, New England, New Brunswick, and Quebec. Yet the West Virginia hares are completely isolated from all others of their kind.

If some mysterious epidemic is responsible for the population crashes, how does it spread from northern populations to the hares stranded on their sky island in West Virginia? In some way or another, all these hares must respond to the same external impulses, for they suffer the same fate at regular intervals. But exactly what the stimuli are, or how they operate, no one has been able to explain.

Glaring at an intruder, a lynx stands guard over the carcass of a deer.

MOUNT McKINLEY
NATIONAL PARK

Mount McKinley National Park, which embraces some three thousand square miles of Alaskan wilderness, is dominated by North America's tallest mountain *(below)*. Mount McKinley's 20,320-foot elevation, in fact, places it in the world-wide elite of just twenty mountains that surpass the 20,000-foot mark. But scenery is only one of Mount McKinley's attractions; the park's wildlife also is unforgettable. Caribou *(left),* with their magnificent branching antlers, wander across the lichen-covered tundra. Grizzly bears *(right)* and timber wolves, both near extinction elsewhere, continue to hold their own in the park. Dall's sheep, lynxes, and golden eagles— all interesting and unusual animals— are some of the other year-round residents of this, the most northerly of our national parks.

PRIMITIVE BIRD

MAMMALLIKE REPTILE

PRIMITIVE REPTILE

FIRST AMPHIBIAN

PRIMITIVE FISH

ANCESTRAL INVERTEBRATE

Of all the backboned animals that live on land, the amphibians—including salamanders, frogs, and toads—have the longest evolutionary history: they arose from a group of primitive fishes some 360 million years ago. The amphibians in turn gave rise to reptiles, the ancestors of birds and mammals.

Salamanders everywhere

Snowshoe hares of Virginia and West Virginia, though isolated, are essentially identical to all others of their kind. They look like snowshoe hares everywhere else, they act like them, and in some mysterious way they even undergo population explosions and collapses at practically the same times as their relatives in other places. But if they remain cut off from all other populations of snowshoe hares for a long enough time, it is just possible that they eventually will develop distinctive characteristics of their own. This we know, for precisely this sort of thing has happened, and is happening, to other kinds of animals.

Take salamanders, for instance. One of the best places in the world for studying salamanders is in southern Appalachia, beyond the line reached by glaciers in the ice age. First of all, salamanders are members of one of the oldest groups of animals with backbones, and so it is natural that the ancient mountains of the East should have a more varied salamander population than do the much younger western mountains. Much of the West, moreover, is unsuitable as a habitat for salamanders, which thrive best in moist forests where winters are moderate and drying winds not too severe. A fairly good variety of salamander species live in the humid mountains of the Pacific Coast, but not nearly so many as are found in the East.

Even in the East, salamanders are rather sparse in glaciated areas. Most of the salamanders in the Northeast were wiped out by the ice sheets, and few species so far have succeeded in reinvading this territory. But south of the ice front, salamanders have flourished relatively undisturbed for millions of years and have constantly been evolving into new forms. One important group, the plethodons, or lungless salamanders, as we have already noted, probably originated in southern Appalachia.

Topography of the southern highlands is ideal for the kind of isolation that leads to variation and change. As we saw at Mount Le Conte, the southern mountains are not high by western standards, but they do rise abruptly from lower bases. Particularly toward the southern end of the Appalachian system, many short ranges and isolated peaks are separated from their neighbors by deep river valleys. The end result is that these peaks and ranges stand as islands; though close together in terms of space, they are separated by barriers that are impassable to creatures that are unable to travel freely over long distances or across extensive areas of unfavorable habitat.

A profusion of plethodons

One group of salamanders found on certain of the southeastern mountains provides a particularly striking example of what can happen in such a situation. All the members of this group are slender, medium-sized forest salamanders that live at high elevations, primarily in the spruce-fir zone. All are lungless; they breathe directly through their moist skins. In every case, the females deposit eggs in damp crevices in rotting logs. Instead of going through a gilled aquatic larval stage, as most salamanders do, the young hatch as fully formed but miniature adults. Thus, in terms of structure, habits, and life history, all are essentially identical. As a result, zoologists have concluded that they all belong to the same species, *Plethodon jordani*, or Jordan's salamanders.

There is only one disturbing element in this neat categorization. Although all these salamanders are basically black, populations inhabiting different peaks or mountain ranges display a wide range of variation in color pattern, so much so that individuals from different areas look like entirely different kinds of salamanders.

The northernmost population of this species, the so-called Metcalf's salamander, is fairly abundant in high mountain forests around Mount Mitchell and all the way north to Virginia. Throughout their range, Metcalf's salamanders are black on their backs and light gray on their undersides. Occasionally, however, an individual is found with traces of white on its sides and back.

Another isolated population of these black plethodons inhabits the higher peaks of the Great Smokies. These, the first members of the group to be discovered, are known as red-cheeked salamanders. As expected, they are basically black, but they differ from Metcalf's salamanders in one startling detail, the bright red patches covering their cheeks.

Red-cheeked salamanders are a specialty of the Great Smokies, and most zoologists who visit the park make a point of looking for them. There is no use in hunting for them in the lowlands, however; they cannot be found down in Sugarlands Cove. But when you climb up to four thousand

A theoretical example shows how climatic change can result in geographical isolation of animal populations. The salamander at the top, an inhabitant of coniferous forests, originally ranged over both mountains. When the climate later warmed, patches of coniferous forests were restricted to the mountaintops; salamanders in each coniferous forest thus became isolated from each other. Scientists speculate that just this sort of thing may have happened to salamander populations in the southern Appalachians.

feet or so, there they are, often in numbers that seem incredible. Although the red-cheeked salamanders are not restricted exclusively to the spruce-fir forests, they certainly seem most at home in such surroundings.

Across the valleys to the southeast of the park, another mountain range, the Nantahalas, rises almost as high as the Smokies. Though near enough for their heavily forested summits to be clearly visible from many points in the park, the mountains are far enough away to support a population of black plethodons that look quite different from the red-cheeked salamanders. Instead of red cheeks, the salamanders of the Nantahalas have bright red legs. Not surprisingly, they are commonly known as red-legged salamanders.

Still another range of mountains, the Unicois, is separated from the Smokies by the valley of the Little Tennessee River, which flows three thousand feet and more below the surrounding summits. Here again there is an isolated population of black plethodons, the so-called Clemson salamanders. These have black backs flecked with conspicuous gray lichenlike patches. The nearby Snowbird Mountains are the home of the so-called Teyahalee salamanders, which look almost like a combination of all the other types, with greenish yellow patches on their cheeks, white spots on their backs, and flecks of red on their legs.

One of the woodland salamanders, *Plethodon jordani,* illustrates how a single species can give rise to a number of subspecies when segments of its population become geographically isolated. The red-cheeked salamander *(below),* the Metcalf's salamander *(opposite page, top),* and the red-legged salamander *(opposite page, bottom)* all are geographical variants of the same species.

What it all means

This could go on and on, for several neighboring mountain masses support still other distinctive populations of the salamander *Plethodon jordani*. How did such a situation come about? All the peaks are essentially alike in climate and topography, and all have many flowering plants, birds, and mammals in common. Why should their salamanders differ?

In every case the salamanders live at or near the summits of their particular mountain masses, primarily in spruce-fir forests. But all the mountains are separated from each other by deep river valleys, too low in elevation to permit the growth of spruce-fir forests. The habitat of the salamanders exists in isolated patches.

At some time in the past, perhaps as recently as the ice age, the various populations of *Plethodon jordani* each became marooned on separate mountain masses. In the beginning, all of them probably looked essentially alike. But as the climate warmed and the lower limits of the spruce-fir forests receded up the mountainsides, all avenues of communication between the various populations were cut off. When contacts between the several groups came to an end, interbreeding among them also ceased. Each population began to follow its own evolutionary path. As variations in color

pattern appeared in individuals on one of these sky islands, they gradually spread throughout the population but could not be passed on to the other groups.

The various populations of *Plethodon jordani* are known as *subspecies*, or *geographical races*: these are groups of individuals of the same species that live within well-defined geographical areas and differ slightly but consistently from populations of the same species living elsewhere. All the subspecies undoubtedly originated from the same ancestral population of salamanders. But since the time of their isolation, each has developed minor variations in color pattern. Given enough time they may evolve more basic biological differences, until each geographical subspecies becomes so distinctive that it will be a full species in its own right.

In a very real sense, then, these isolated mountain masses are islands in the sky. As a matter of fact, Charles Darwin's revolutionary thoughts on the evolution of species were prompted by his observations of a very similar situation. On a voyage along the coast of South America, Darwin visited the Galápagos Islands, an isolated island chain west of Ecuador. On each of the major islands, he found a population of finchlike birds, all of them such poor fliers that they were effectively isolated from similar birds on nearby islands. All were obviously related, but each population differed in some respect from the birds on every other island.

As he mulled over these observations, Darwin eventually

The various subspecies of the salamander *Plethodon jordani* each live in restricted geographical areas in the southern Appalachians. Although their ranges may be separated by distances of only a few miles, areas of unsuitable habitat serve as effective barriers to contacts among the populations.

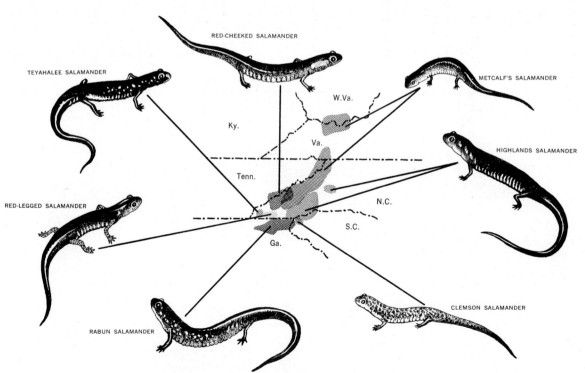

realized what was happening. Like the salamanders we have been discussing, the isolated populations of Galápagos finches were evolving into new species.

New trees from old

Animals, of course, are not alone in showing the effects of isolation; plants are also molded by such situations. Balsam fir, for instance, ranges clear across the northern part of North America. This belt of fir forest extends without a break from Maine to Alaska. And all the way across the continent, balsam fir remains balsam fir; eastern trees and western trees are identical in every respect.

But isolated fir stands also extend south into the Appalachians. They undoubtedly are remnants of more extensive fir forests that were pushed southward along the mountains during the ice age. In West Virginia, for example, balsam firs persist here and there around upland sphagnum bogs. These firs show variations from the firs found farther north, but the differences are minor, not enough to justify placing the trees in a separate species.

Farther south, however, the effects of isolation are unmistakably evident. In the islands of fir forest on the summits of the Smokies and nearby mountains, the trees are slightly but consistently different from firs found anywhere else. One of the most important variations is in the shape of the scales making up the fir cones. Any modification in a plant's reproductive organs is significant so far as its classification is concerned. In this case, the cones have become so distinctive that botanists have concluded that the firs of southern Appalachia must indeed be regarded as a new and different species, Fraser balsam fir.

Much the same thing has happened to eastern hemlocks. Most of the hemlocks in southern Appalachia are typical eastern hemlocks. Yet in a remnant population in the southern Blue Ridge Mountains, the trees differ slightly from other hemlocks. They still resemble eastern hemlocks in a general way, but they have longer needles and bear much larger cones. These Carolina hemlocks, as they are called, have become so distinctive, in fact, that they must certainly be considered a separate species. Again, the evolutionary paths of two trees have diverged, and our forests have been enriched as a result.

EASTERN HEMLOCK

CAROLINA HEMLOCK

Hemlocks demonstrate that plants as well as animals can evolve new species as a result of isolation. The wide-ranging eastern hemlock bears half-inch-long needles and one-inch-long cones. The Carolina hemlock occurs only in a small area in the Blue Ridge Mountains. Conspicuously longer needles and cones on trees in this remnant population distinguish the Carolina hemlock as a separate species.

Western islands

By this time you may be wondering if islands of isolated plant and animal populations exist only on eastern mountains. Of course this is not so. The restricted areas of arctic-alpine plants on the summits of the San Francisco Peaks are true sky islands. So, in another sense, is the bottom of the Grand Canyon, with its lower-Sonoran plants and animals. Like mountains almost everywhere, the great mountain

Like islands in a sea of grass, the Chiricahua Mountains rise out of the desert of southwestern Arizona. Less than three hundred miles separate the Chiricahuas from the San Francisco Peaks, yet the two ranges support markedly different populations of plants and animals.

ranges of the West support isolated populations and endemic races of plants and animals.

One mountainous area in the West is especially worth visiting. It is so different from the rest of the United States that it is nearly unique. In extreme southeastern Arizona, a number of isolated rocky masses rise abruptly from the desert. Some of them—the Chiricahua Mountains, the Huachucas, the Santa Catalinas, and the Santa Ritas—have steep craggy peaks that stand six thousand feet and more above the surrounding desert.

The Chiricahuas, one of the more southerly of these mountain groups, afford a particularly good example of what can

138

happen in such a situation. The mountains are spread over an area about thirty miles long and fifteen miles wide, and the highest peaks reach nine thousand feet above sea level. Much of the range is included in Coronado National Forest, while one section of unusually picturesque rock formations has been set aside as Chiricahua National Monument.

In terms of miles it is not far from the Chiricahuas to the San Francisco Peaks, yet in terms of the life they support the two mountain masses lie worlds apart. The San Franciscos

are related to the Rockies, detached perhaps, but sharing many characteristics in common with that great mountain system to the north. The mountains of southeastern Arizona, on the other hand, actually are isolated outposts of the Sierra Madre Occidental, one of the great mountain chains of Mexico. On the lower slopes of the San Franciscos, we observed a bit of spillover across the Mexican border; in these more southerly mountains, Mexican influences dominate—in terms of trees, wild flowers, reptiles, and almost every other form of life. The Chiricahuas are sky islands all right, but they are Mexican islands, not matched by any others in the United States.

CHIRICAHUA NATIONAL MONUMENT

Strangely beautiful rock formations, etched into fantastic shapes by the action of wind and water, are a major attraction of the seventeen-square-mile portion of the Chiricahua range that was set aside as a national monument in 1924. One of the formations rises 137 feet high; another consists of a 652-ton boulder perched atop a four-foot pedestal of rock. Other attractions include thousand-foot-deep canyons, natural caves decorated with prehistoric Indian paintings, and many plants and animals that have strayed across the border from Mexico. Visitor accommodations within the national monument include hiking trails, picnic areas, campgrounds, and a ranch that offers meals and lodging.

How to visit Mexico without leaving the United States

More than any other group of living things, birds typify the Mexican flavor of the Chiricahuas, perhaps because birds can fly and therefore can more easily extend their ranges to out-of-the-way corners of appropriate habitat. In any case, the entire area is famous as a mecca for ornithologists; it includes more bird species from south of the border than almost any other area in the United States.

An ideal starting point for an exploration of the ornithological wonders of the Chiricahuas is Cave Creek Canyon. The approach to this eastern gateway to the mountains is through arid range country, with a rolling landscape covered with a scattering of scrubby semidesert plants such as creosote bushes, mesquites, and coarse grasses. But when you enter the cool, well-watered canyon, you are confronted by a scene of utter contrast. Because of the almost magical influence of water in a dry land, the vegetation suddenly is more varied, taller, denser, and more robust. And the banks of Cave Creek itself are lined with tall, healthy trees—western sycamores, Arizona walnuts, live oaks, and many more.

Overhead the trees are alive with Bullock's orioles, western tanagers, and other birds that are common throughout much of the Southwest. All are attractive and well worth watching, but you are looking for other more special residents of the canyon. And in the sycamores you are likely to find them—noisy, conspicuous birds that perch on branches from which they can easily dive for unsuspecting insects. They are sulphur-bellied flycatchers, readily recognized by their brownish tails and streaky yellow breasts. In the United States they breed only in the Chiricahuas and a few other places in southern Arizona. Most of their kin dwell in remote mountain canyons south of the Mexican border.

Bridled titmice, handsome little birds with jaunty crests and black-and-white striped cheeks, also may be feeding nearby; they, too, are Mexican specialties. But the real prize among the southern birds that nest in wooded canyons in

Spiny yuccas grow among the walnuts, live oaks, and
other broadleaf trees that flourish in Cave Creek Canyon,
a popular approach to the Chiricahua Mountains. Since
Mexico is only fifty miles away, the entire range is a
bird watcher's paradise, for it abounds in species seldom
found anywhere else in the United States.

143

Pert western tanagers brighten the western mountain forests from Alaska to Mexico. These gay sparrow-sized birds augment their insect diet with fruit, a trait that makes them unpopular with California cherry growers.

the Chiricahuas, Santa Ritas, and Huachucas is the coppery-tailed trogon. Males of these foot-long tropical beauties are greenish on their backs and rich rosy red on their breasts, while their heads are black and their tails are coppery bronze. Females are browner, with less red and green, but spectacular just the same. Although trogons probably nest in the canyon every year, you may not discover their haunts, since the birds are never abundant. But if you do find them, you will have seen one of the loveliest and most famous residents of this Mexican island in the sky.

Many plants on the Chiricahua slopes also hint of southern influences. Between 5500 and 6500 feet, rolling terraces beside the stream are practically covered by stands of stunted oak trees. This forest type is widespread in Mexico's Sierra Madre, where it is known as *encinal*. A little farther up the slopes, tall pines become intermixed with the scrubby oaks. Here again you see a link with the South; most of the conifers are Chihuahua and Apache pines, Mexican relatives of ponderosas. Game is plentiful in this mixed forest, but you should look especially for the elusive, curiously patterned harlequin quails and the big, swift-flying band-tailed pigeon. Both will require some hunting; they are heard far more often than they are seen.

A bit closer to the summits the slopes are taken over by pure stands of true ponderosa pines. This forest closely resembles the ponderosa pine belt on the San Franciscos, but with some interesting differences in bird life. It is one of the few areas in the United States where you can expect to find Mexican juncos, trusting little birds with conspicuous and distinctive bright yellow eyes. Chickadees that call from the treetops sound much like chickadees everywhere, but they, too, seem somehow different. They have much more black on their throats and breasts than other chickadees do, and their grayish flanks show no trace of brown. These birds are Mexican chickadees, and you are seeing them in the only place they are known to be found north of the Mexican border.

As you might expect, this forest also has a special warbler, common but difficult to spot. High in the pines are olive warblers, birds so different from other wood warblers that some specialists consider them members of a separate family. Their bodies are dull gray, but the males have bright orange-brown heads and striking black cheek patches. Again,

A visit to the southern Arizona mountains may yield a glimpse of the rare coppery-tailed trogon, here portrayed among the branches of a western sycamore. The upper bird is a male; the lower one is a female. The Spanish name for the trogon is "coa-coa," in imitation of its harsh, croaking call.

these are primarily Central American birds; only here and in a few other places in Arizona and New Mexico do olive warblers ever stray north of the border.

A return to Canada

As you approach the Chiricahua summits, you will at last leave Mexico far behind. Do not expect to see bridled titmice, trogons, or olive warblers on the mountaintops, but look instead for ruby-crowned kinglets and hermit thrushes. Forget about Apache pines and encinal; here the land is cloaked with aspen and Douglasfir, much like the forests you saw on the San Francisco slopes and much as you would find at higher elevations throughout the West.

Mexico lies only fifty miles away, and great deserts spread about the bases of the mountains. But your surroundings look for all the world like an isolated bit of Canadian-zone landscape. You are truly on an island in the sky.

For mountains everywhere, in one sense or another, are like islands. Every mountain or range of mountains has an individuality all its own. Many of them even boast populations of special animals and plants that live only on their slopes and nowhere else in the world. Yet most of them also share many residents in common, plants and animals that are able to live far beyond their usual ranges only because the land rises abruptly in elevation. And in every case, the life on the mountains differs strikingly from life found in the nearby lowlands.

Mountains are special, then, and different in almost every way. To see new things or to discover familiar forms in unfamiliar surroundings; to breathe cooler, fresher air; to widen your horizons and your understanding—these are just a few of the rewards that come to anyone who would venture upward to these islands in the sky.

For anyone interested in the world of nature, the mountains are a wonderland beyond compare. Because of the highly specialized living conditions found in mountain country, the strange and the familiar often blend in unexpected combinations that delight the senses and challenge the mind.

147

A Variety of Mountains

On our brief visits to a few of the American highlands, we have seen how mountains everywhere are the same in certain respects but at the same time differ as a result of variations in their geographical locations and geological histories. Yet so far we have barely scratched the surface. Great mountain chains, less elevated ridges, and isolated highlands are scattered all across the face of the continent. Almost everywhere in the country, mountains of one sort or another can be reached within a day or so of traveling time.

Some of them—the Cumberlands, the Catskills, the Cascades, and the Sierra Nevadas—are so rich with history and folklore that their names are familiar to Americans everywhere. Others such as the Kittatinnies in the East or the Wichitas and Wallowas farther west are less famous, but they are worth exploring just the same. Certainly we cannot visit all the uplands in the United States—that would require a lifetime of travel. But a quick tour of a few of them will provide at least a hint of the variety and fascination of America's mountains.

MAJOR MOUNTAIN RANGES
OF THE UNITED STATES

0   100   200   300   400
Statute miles

© 1958, JEPPESEN & CO. DENVER, COLO., U.S.A.
ALL RIGHTS RESERVED
REVISED 5-67

Where hawks fly by

The Kittatinny Mountains, a chain of low ridges that angles across eastern Pennsylvania, are modest mountains by any standard. Little would seem to set them apart from other highlands in the central Appalachians. Taller mountains can be found not far away, and several nearby ridges command more dramatic vistas of the Pennsylvania landscape. Yet it is a narrow spur on the southern Kittatinnies —not the neighboring highlands—that attracts visitors by the thousands every autumn.

This bit of mountainscape, which has been set aside and preserved by a group of conservationists as Hawk Mountain Sanctuary, overlooks one of the greatest spectacles of bird migration to be seen anywhere in the world. Every year from late August until mid-November, southward-bound hawks soar by within easy viewing range of the mountaintops. Sometimes thousands of birds pass in a single day, and their numbers climb to the tens of thousands over the course of a season.

The Appalachians have long been famous as an avenue for bird migrations. Perhaps these conspicuous topographical features, running in a generally north-south direction, help

Every autumn, bird watchers gather atop Hawk Mountain, Pennsylvania, to witness the migration flights of hawks and other birds that pass the peak on their way south for winter. Spring flights also occur, but the birds are less concentrated then, and timing of their flights is less predictable.

to orient the birds as they make their way up and down the continent. Even more important, the mountains create strong and dependable rising air currents. As surface air flows against the steep mountain ridges, it is deflected into enormous updrafts that help keep the birds aloft, especially in the case of large soaring hawks.

A number of other Appalachian ridges are notable vantage points for observing migration flights, but Hawk Mountain certainly is the best. Several ridges converge at this point on the southern Kittatinnies. As a result, migrating birds from a vast territory to the north are funneled past the narrow ridge at Hawk Mountain.

Hunters were the first to discover this autumn spectacle, and every year they gathered on the ridge and slaughtered hawks by the thousands. But eventually public outrage reached such a pitch that a group of conservationists finally were able to raise enough money to purchase the mountain and create the sanctuary. As a result of their educational campaigns, it is now illegal to shoot these beautiful, valuable birds in many states. People still flock to Hawk Mountain every fall, but now they carry binoculars instead of guns.

A day on Hawk Mountain

Anyone can visit this famous sanctuary; it is a short, easy climb from the parking lot at the base of the mountain to its rocky crest. Seek a sheltered spot before you settle down to watch, since autumn breezes are brisk on the ridge. Your observation point, moreover, should face northeastward, for that is the direction from which most of the approaching hawks will first appear.

Heavy flights do not necessarily occur every day, and even experienced observers cannot always predict when hawks will be plentiful. Yet almost any day from mid-September to mid-October is likely to produce a good flight, and there is always the possibility that you will hit one of those banner days when thousands of birds drift by. Even the best time of day is not entirely predictable. Sometimes the best flights occur early in the morning; occasionally they come toward evening. But normally the hawks begin to fly toward midmorning as the sun grows warm and air currents begin to rise along the mountain's flanks. The

Records kept over many years provide a timetable for migrations at Hawk Mountain. The length of each bar indicates duration of the species' migration period; darker areas indicate the peak migration times.

153

heaviest flights usually pass Hawk Mountain between eleven o'clock in the morning and one or two o'clock in the afternoon.

As you scan the sky through your binoculars, your first hint that the birds are on the move probably will be the appearance of a tiny speck against the northeastern sky. As the bird moves nearer, you notice that it has short, broad wings and its underside is tinged with rusty red. Then you see that its fan-shaped tail is boldly banded with light and dark stripes. There can be no doubt that it is a broad-winged hawk, the species that is most plentiful early in the season. Buoyed up by the rising currents of warm air, the bird glides easily past with scarcely a flap of its wings, and disappears finally into the southern sky. It may have been a local Pennsylvania bird, but it could just as easily have been on its way south from the forests of Quebec or Nova Scotia.

Although September flights consist mainly of broad-winged hawks, other species are certain to pass as well. Now and then you may spot a swiftly flying sparrow hawk or a large and graceful osprey. Sharp-shinned and Cooper's hawks also flash by with strong, rapid wingbeats. By

The crow-sized broad-winged hawk, which winters in South America and nests as far north as Quebec, is the most common species to be seen at Hawk Mountain. On a record-breaking September day in 1948, more than eleven thousand of the birds soared past the Pennsylvania peak.

October most of the broad-winged hawks will be gone, but in their place you will see great numbers of red-shouldered and red-tailed hawks. With luck, you may even glimpse a peregrine falcon; most of these birds have been exterminated in the eastern mountains, but a few still survive in the far-northern wilderness.

For unknown reasons, an occasional day on the heights may yield no hawks at all. Yet even then there is plenty to see on Hawk Mountain. Early in the day hundreds of warblers often pass within easy viewing range, for if flight conditions are good, these normally nocturnal migrants sometimes prolong their movements into the morning hours. Blue jays, cedar waxwings, rose-breasted grosbeaks, and small groups of turkey vultures often fly by. Later in the season, wedges of Canada geese also make their way southward along the mountain chains. If all else fails, you can watch the antics of the resident ravens. No day on the overlook ever is completely wasted.

And whenever you visit Hawk Mountain or any other observation point along the Appalachian ridges, you hope

The peregrine falcon, slightly larger than the broad-winged hawk, is one of the fastest of all birds. In normal flight it commonly reaches about 80 miles per hour, but in its "stoop," or dive toward prey, it can exceed 175 miles per hour.

Because of a greatly exaggerated reputation for preying on chickens, the red-tailed hawk has been relentlessly persecuted by humans. In reality, it is of inestimable value to farmers, for, as in the case of most hawks, its major source of food is mice and other destructive rodents.

that your day may be crowned by the sighting of a bald eagle. They are much larger than the other hawks, and adults have snowy white heads and tails that form a striking contrast with their dark bodies.

Throughout most of the United States, bald eagles now are rare. Because of illegal shooting and other pressures of civilization, fewer and fewer of these majestic birds are seen each year. They remain abundant only in Alaska. But even if they were common, their wild beauty still would be a thrilling sight. If you should see one soaring overhead on wings that span about seven feet, you will know that your day on Hawk Mountain has reached a fitting climax.

Midcontinent mountains

Of all places in the country to look for mountains, southwestern Oklahoma would seem to be one of the least promising territories. Yet even here a range of gently rolling mountains, the Wichitas, rises from the surrounding sea of grasslands. They are not high mountains; the tallest peak,

Mount Scott, reaches only 2464 feet above sea level. Even so, its summit stands a thousand feet above its surroundings, high enough to command a splendid view of rolling plains and prairies.

Despite their modest proportions, the Wichitas are virtually unique: they bear a distinct—and distinctive—flavor of the Old West. Sixty thousand acres of these pleasant uplands have been set aside as the Wichita Mountains Wildlife Refuge. When you visit this living museum, you will have the feeling that the clock has been turned back one hundred years or more, for the hills are filled with sights like those that greeted pioneers traveling west over the old Santa Fe Trail.

Your first hint of the distinctive character of the Wichitas comes almost as soon as you enter the refuge. After driving through a narrow canyon, you emerge suddenly on an open grassland hemmed in by a series of low hills. And there, all about the small lake at the center of the opening, you see scores of bison. The animals that have been preserved at Wichita Mountains Wildlife Refuge form one of the few surviving remnants of the gigantic herds of bison that once roamed the western plains.

The majestic bald eagle, soaring on wings that span seven feet, is an unforgettable sight. Yet fewer and fewer of our national birds are seen each year. Illegal shooting, the destruction of nesting sites, and the effects of chemical pesticides all have taken their toll of bald eagles.

If you have never seen a living bison before, they will probably seem even more massive and wild-looking than you had ever imagined they would. Old bulls, in particular, are tremendous, with great humped shoulders and enormous heads. Females, much smaller, are likely to be accompanied by yellowish red calves in summer. Do not be tempted to leave your car and approach for a close-up photograph, however. Bison may look placid, but they are still wild animals, fast on their feet and extremely dangerous when they are annoyed.

If you can shift your attention from these legendary beasts, you will find another Wichita Mountains specialty. The cattle grazing on the nearby hills are authentic long-horns—slim-flanked, agile animals crowned by magnificent horns that often span seven feet or more from tip to tip.

They are direct descendants of the fighting range cattle that the Spanish brought to the New World and exactly the same as the cattle that made up the famous trail herds of the Old West. The herd preserved at the Wichita Mountains Wildlife Refuge—usually about 350 strong—is the largest herd of longhorns still in existence.

A number of prairie-dog towns also are scattered across the refuge lands. These busy little rodents, which live in colonies that often cover several acres, seem to be always in motion. Heads are constantly popping up from the entrances to their elaborately branching underground burrows. The prairie dogs pause for a moment on the mounds outside their dens and sit up on their haunches to scan the landscape. Then, if no danger threatens, they begin to nibble on grasses and other plants nearby. But if an enemy

The bison herd at Oklahoma's Wichita Mountains Wildlife Refuge, now maintained at about one thousand head, was begun with six bulls and nine cows imported from the New York Zoological Park in 1907, when bison were almost extinct. Now, thanks to protection and careful management, the great beasts once again are plentiful on a number of refuges scattered throughout western North America.

appears—perhaps a Swainson's hawk flying overhead—they bark shrill warnings to their neighbors and scamper for cover.

You probably will be tempted to watch the antics of these plump ground squirrels for hours on end, but there are too many other things to see at the refuge: wild turkeys, coyotes, jack rabbits, herds of white-tailed deer, majestic elk, and even a few pronghorns. Most of these animals can be seen nearly anywhere on the Great Plains, yet the Wichita Mountains also harbor a few rather unexpected residents, creatures whose existence in these grasslands hinges directly on the presence of mountains.

Rocky ravines and canyons in the refuge often echo with the songs of rock wrens and canyon wrens, two species that are more common farther west. In the midcontinent grasslands, they nest only where they can find canyons, steep cliffs, and rising land. Another characteristic bird on Mount Scott and other exposed summits is the rufous-crowned sparrow. The race found in the Wichitas is better known as the rock sparrow, and no bird ever was more appropriately named. These little red-capped sparrows are constantly creeping through crevices, along ledges, and into any convenient openings on the cliffs where they live.

Golden eagles, big golden-brown relatives of bald eagles, also nest on the rocky cliffs of Mount Scott. If you spend any time at all on the heights, you are quite likely to see at least one. But again, they live here only because the land rises abruptly in elevation. Areas of the Great Plains that have no mountains have no golden eagles.

Thus, the Wichita Mountains support a curious mixture of living things. Because of their location and modest size, the slopes are inhabited primarily by creatures that we normally think of as belonging to the plains. At the same time, they shelter a few typical mountain-dwelling animals that simply could not survive on the vast flatlands surrounding the summits.

Unlike the bald eagle, which builds its bulky nest in dead trees, usually in coastal areas, the golden eagle raises its young on rocky ledges in mountain country. Along with many other essentially beneficial birds of prey, the golden eagle has been ruthlessly persecuted by humans.

Land of many peaks

The Colorado Rockies are part of the complex Rocky Mountain system, a chain of about twenty interlocking ranges stretching from Alberta, Canada, south to New Mexico. In Colorado, hundreds of Rocky Mountain peaks exceed ten thousand feet, and many soar to more than fourteen thousand feet.

Several other mountain groups interrupt the level horizons of the midcontinent region. There are the Ozarks of Missouri and Arkansas, ancient mountains that closely resemble the Appalachians. In Oklahoma and Arkansas, the Ouachitas and other low mountains rise in crumpled masses from the flatlands. The rugged terrain of the Black Hills of South Dakota forms a meeting place where life forms from the East and West merge and intermix. All are interesting and well worth visiting. But by now you are certain to be wondering about the really big mountain ranges of the United States—the Rockies, the Sierra Nevadas, and the volcanic peaks of the Cascades.

A good place to begin exploring the great mountains of the West is in Colorado, where more peaks exceed fourteen thousand feet than in any other state in the country. About sixty percent of Colorado is covered by great ranges of the Rocky Mountains, lying in more or less parallel rows with vast parklike valleys in between.

162

One particularly fine tract of the Colorado Rockies has been preserved as Rocky Mountain National Park. If you approach the park from the east, the snow-capped peaks of the Rockies will be visible from miles away across the plains. But when you reach the foothills, the transition from flatlands to mountains is abrupt. One moment you are on the plains, the next you begin climbing through Big Thompson or some other canyon. When you emerge from the canyon, a couple of thousand feet higher than the level at the start of your climb, you are in Estes Park, squarely at the foot of Longs Peak.

Like a number of similar areas in the southern Rockies, Estes Park is not a man-made park at all; it just happens to look like one. It is a huge intermontane valley surrounded by tall peaks and perched high above the lowlands. The open grasslands of the valley are interspersed with groves of ponderosa pines that look as if they had been deliberately planted. Towering overhead is 14,256-foot-high Longs Peak, the tallest in the national park, and on the far side of the valley is the entrance to the park itself.

HAYMAKER OF THE HEIGHTS

Almost anywhere in the Rockies, a high-pitched bleating sound coming from the debris in a rockslide may announce the presence of a pika. This active little creature, about the size and shape of a guinea pig, is a relative of rabbits and hares. Since it does not hibernate, the pika's chief concern is sustaining itself through the bleak mountain winter. During late summer, it busily harvests a variety of plant materials, cures them in the sun, and then stores them in the rocky labyrinth where it makes its home. Thus provided for, the pika passes the winter undaunted by the snowdrifts that drive many other animals to lower altitudes.

Pikas, which live at altitudes up to twelve thousand feet, make their homes among piles of fallen rocks, where they can find ready refuge from swooping hawks and eagles.

A pika's "haystack" may contain a bushel or more of dried plants. Most of the pika's winter hoard is gathered within one hundred feet of its home.

The pika is closely related to hares and rabbits but lacks their long ears and conspicuous tails.

On Trail Ridge Road

Once you enter the park, the road begins to climb in earnest. It quickly passes out of the ponderosa pine forest, skirts a number of beaver ponds, and enters a forest of Douglasfirs where you may see bull elk, or in autumn hear their bugling. At about the two-mile level, the road passes through dense stands of spirelike Engelmann spruces. But you keep climbing, for your objective is the highest section of Trail Ridge Road. For mile after mile, this fabulous highway remains above timber line, following the route of an old Indian trail across the summits.

At eleven thousand feet you finally reach the Rainbow Curve Overlook, and here you stop in another world, the one above forests. Spreading before you is an indescribable panorama of mountain slopes, jagged peaks, and the incredibly vast expanse of the Great Plains. But as you gaze at the vista, you are soon distracted by activities nearer at hand. All about the parking area, golden-mantled ground squirrels appear as if from nowhere. These sleek, inquisitive little rodents, which look something like overgrown chipmunks, are common in mountain areas throughout the West.

Pikas, sometimes known as conies or little chief hares, also are common among rockslides near and above timber line. These small, short-eared relatives of rabbits live in openings among the rocks, but they spend enough time on the surface to be easily observed.

All through the brief mountain summer, the industrious little pikas are busy harvesting hay. Unlike ground squirrels, which hibernate in winter, pikas are active throughout the year. Just as tree squirrels store nuts, pikas prepare for winter by storing dried plants. With their sharp front teeth, they snip off grasses, sedges, wild flowers, and even twigs, and then they spread their crops on stones in the sun to dry. When rain threatens, they scurry among the rocks and carry their precious harvest, a mouthful at a time, to the shelter of their rock piles.

Yellow-bellied marmots, near relatives of woodchucks, also thrive above tree line, although they range down to

Rolled into a compact heat-conserving ball, the golden-mantled ground squirrel avoids the rigors of winter by hibernating in the depths of its burrow. In this sleeplike state, body processes such as heartbeat and respiration slow down drastically and the animal subsists on the energy stored in its body as fat.

The golden-mantled ground squirrel, common throughout the foothills and mountains of the West, is often mistaken for a chipmunk, but the absence of facial stripes readily distinguishes it from its smaller relative.

much lower elevations as well. Like pikas, the marmots harvest some plants for winter, and they have the added advantage of going into the deep sleep of hibernation during the coldest months of the year.

One of the few large mammals seen above timber line in this area is the mountain sheep, found from time to time in small bands on the rocky summits. Here they do not linger beside the road as they do in some other places. If you see them at all, they probably will be so far away that you will need binoculars to watch them.

On the mountain meadows

In surprising contrast with eastern mountains, the much more extensive areas above timber line on these western summits harbor quite a few birds. Ravens, Clark's nutcrackers, gray jays, white-crowned sparrows, and water pipits all are seen from time to time. After their nesting season, flocks of mountain bluebirds visit the crests, and Swainson's hawks cruise overhead in search of unwary squirrels and pikas.

Brown-capped rosy finches, large brownish sparrows tinged with pink on their wings and rumps, are especially common. They congregate at the margins of melting snow-

An avid bird watcher scans the barren summit of a peak in Colorado's Rocky Mountain National Park, hopeful that he will glimpse a few of the birds that visit the alpine tundra to feed on plants, insects, or small mammals.

fields, where insects are likely to be chilled to inactivity and new supplies of seeds are constantly being uncovered. Alarm them and the whole flock takes off in rapid flight, their wings whistling musically as they go. The finches usually nest in dark sheltered crevices on rock ledges near the highest point on Trail Ridge Road, just above twelve thousand feet. But the nests are so well concealed that you are unlikely to discover one unless you happen to spot an adult returning to feed its young.

The finest arctic specialties of the windswept Colorado summits are white-tailed ptarmigans, small grouse that remain on the treeless heights throughout the year. In summer their bodies are neatly camouflaged with mottled grays and browns, a near-perfect match for the background of stones and dried grasses where they live. Ask a park naturalist how to recognize these birds and he is quite likely to tell you, "If you see a rock that gets up and walks away, it was a ptarmigan."

Even in winter ptarmigans remain nearly invisible. Like snowshoe hares, they molt their grays and browns in autumn and don new coats of pure white. Fringes of long feathers on their toes serve as effective snowshoes. With no trouble at all, the ptarmigans walk across the snowy summits, seeking places where the wind has exposed the nutritious buds of low-growing willows, birches, and aspens.

The white-tailed ptarmigan, one of the largest birds to be found on windswept mountaintops of the West, descends below timber line only when deep snow covers the alpine plants on which it feeds. This one is in the process of molting from winter-white to summer-brown.

The alpine forget-me-not usually can be identified at a glance by its brilliant blue flowers; occasionally, however, the plant produces pure white blossoms. This dweller on the heights is at its best on exposed crests and ridges between nine and twelve thousand feet.

The ptarmigans depend heavily on their concealing colors and seem quite fearless. You generally have to come so near that you practically step on the birds before they become alarmed and flee. Even the chicks are so well camouflaged that they seem to disappear before your eyes. If you see a hen in mid-July, watch her patiently. After a time she may cluck once or twice, and then, almost beneath your feet, the young will appear as if from nowhere.

One of the dividends that comes with searching for ptarmigans in the mountain meadows is the opportunity to roam through colorful alpine gardens. Pioneers among the wild flowers begin to bloom as soon as the snow has melted, but the height of the spectacle comes in late July and August. One of the first to appear is the yellow-flowered glacier lily, a handsome western relative of trout lilies, or dogtooth violets. Early in the season acre upon acre of alpine meadow is carpeted with glacier lilies, but even late in summer stragglers continue to bloom about the margins of melting snowbanks.

Some, such as gentians, alpine avens, and sky pilot, range all the way south to the San Franciscos, but there are others that we have not seen before. American bistort, for instance, bears clusters of tiny white flowers, like tufts of cotton, on slender stems that sway gently in the breeze. Moss campion grows in dense cushionlike mats among the rocks, and rosecrown, topped with clumps of pink cloverlike blossoms, pushes its fleshy stems and leaves up through moist crevices. White camas, alpine buttercup, forget-me-not, alpine sunflower—the possibilities are so varied that you probably will need a guidebook to identify the profusion of colorful blooms. And the spectacle is so overwhelming that long after you leave Trail Ridge Road, the patchwork of color on the alpine summits may well prove to be your most enduring recollection of Rocky Mountain National Park.

The northern Rockies

To the north of Colorado, the Rocky Mountains include many more ranges and many other mountain parks. Each one has its own distinctive personality and unique attrac-

Flecked with delicate pink stars, each about a quarter of an inch across, the moss campion often grows side by side with the alpine forget-me-not. Like its companion, it sometimes puts forth white flowers. Both plants exhibit the low, cushionlike growth habit that typifies many alpine wild flowers.

tions. Grand Teton National Park in northwestern Wyoming,
for example, boasts what many people contend are the most
beautiful mountains in the country. Certainly the Grand
Tetons are dramatic. Their jagged saw-toothed peaks jut
against the sky, rising abruptly for seven thousand feet
from the valley, known as Jackson Hole, at their feet.

Bands of mountain sheep pick their way across the
crumpled rocky masses, and the valley at the base of the
Tetons is world-famous as a game preserve. Great herds of
elk gather in Jackson Hole each winter, and every summer
rare and beautiful trumpeter swans nest on Jackson Lake.
Here you can expect to see moose, mule deer, porcupines,
black and grizzly bears, and a hundred other sights.

But above all, the Tetons are famous as a mountain
climber's paradise. All ten of the Teton peaks are difficult
climbs, requiring careful preparation, special mountaineering skills, and plenty of experience. No one strolls to the
summit of Grand Teton or Mount Moran. Yet those who
have made it to the top claim that getting there was half
the fun.

With their dramatic contours uninterrupted by any foothills, the Grand Tetons rise in stark grandeur from low-lying valleys in Wyoming and Idaho. The highest peak, Mount Moran, is 12,594 feet high. Ice-age glaciers sculptured the sheer walls and jagged crests that make the Tetons a mecca for mountain climbers.

Just to the north of Jackson Hole is another famous park, Yellowstone, the oldest national park in the world. Yellowstone, of course, is best known for Old Faithful and its other geysers and hot springs, yet these actually account for only a fraction of the park's attractions. Thousands of acres of true mountain wilderness are included in the park, land that serves as sanctuary for everything from grizzly bears, bison, mountain lions, and mountain sheep to delicate Rocky Mountain fringed gentians and calypso orchids.

Still farther to the north, on the Canadian border of Montana, is Glacier National Park, not quite so famous as Yellowstone. Although a number of small glaciers still exist in the area, the park was set aside mainly as a showcase for evidence of past glacial activity. Broad sweeping valleys, huge natural amphitheaters gouged from the sides of mountains, and crystal-clear lakes perched high on the slopes all contribute to the magnificence of the park's scenery. All were formed by the great glaciers that swept across this northland in the recent geologic past.

Because the park is so far north, timber line is located

TO CLIMB A MOUNTAIN

Why do men climb mountains? No single
explanation can account for the fascination
that heights hold for so many people. Yet
much of the lure of the mountains
undoubtedly lies in man's desire to pit his
strength, courage, and ingenuity against the
most formidable obstacles nature has to offer.
For mountaineering offers challenges—and
satisfactions—that are not available through
any other endeavor. In addition to the
obvious physical demands of stamina,
coordination, and agility, climbing calls for
coolness, discipline, and the ability to
respond quickly to the unexpected—qualities
that often remain undeveloped by the
humdrum routine of everyday life. But for
those who master the specialized techniques
of mountain climbing, the rewards are
undeniable. The pictures here and on the
following pages offer a hint of the thrills that
await all who are skillful and daring enough
to accept the challenges posed by sheer rock
walls and high places.

Although most members of its family are associated with the tropics, the gay calypso orchid thrives in cool coniferous forests throughout much of North America.

at relatively low elevations, only six thousand feet or so above sea level. Thousand-acre alpine meadows, patched with snow and glacial ice all summer long, spread out in every direction. Here you can expect to see ptarmigans, gray-crowned rosy finches, marmots, and ground squirrels.

Most of the flowers will be familiar to anyone who has traveled the Trail Ridge Road, but the park also includes two handsome species that do not range so far south as Colorado. One is a yellow-flowered paintbrush that dots the slopes with splashes of color during a long blooming season. The other is bear grass, a member of the lily family that flourishes on some of the Pacific Coast mountains also. It grows on lower slopes as well as in alpine meadows but seems to be at its best just below timber line. The dense clusters of tiny white flowers blooming at the tips of slender two- to three-foot-tall stems are such a common sight that bear grass is an unofficial floral trademark for Glacier National Park.

But if bear grass is the floral symbol of the park, the mountain goat is surely its best known animal. These northern Rocky Mountain peaks are among the few places in the United States where mountain goats are found. Zoologists will tell you that they are not goats at all, but are much more closely related to certain of the antelopes. No matter—they certainly look like shaggy white goats. Their humped shoulders are about three and a half feet high; they have short, slender horns; and the males even have long beards like those of goats.

Mountain sheep, also found in the park, are often seen in the lowlands and along highways, but the goats stay almost exclusively on the wildest heights. As with the sheep, their hoofs are well adapted for sure-footed climbing and leaping over rugged, uneven terrain. Though you very rarely will see the goats at close range, you soon will learn to watch for their shaggy forms high on the rock summits as they pick their way across alpine meadows and explore narrow ledges in search of twigs, grass, and other foods.

From the Sierras to Mount Rainier

It may be difficult to leave the Rockies, with their wealth of history, wildlife, and natural beauty. Yet nearly one-third of the continent—and many other mountains—lies

Bear grass flourishes in high-altitude meadows and forest clearings throughout Glacier National Park. Each plant must grow for five to seven years before producing its showy three-foot-tall stalks of flowers; in the meantime, its tough grasslike leaves provide an important winter food for the park's famous mountain goats.

Long a symbol of remote, inaccessible heights, mountain goats are found in the northern Rocky Mountains from Alaska to central Idaho. These close relatives of the chamois of Europe actually are not goats at all, but belong instead to the antelope family.

MASTERS OF THE MOUNTAINTOP

Prancing along incredibly narrow ledges or picking
their way across steep slopes littered with rocky
rubble, the nimble mountain goats find safety by
traveling where no predator dares to follow. Even
in winter the goats spend much of their time on
the heights, grazing on withered tundra plants that
have been exposed by the wind. Unlike mountain
sheep, the goats have never been seriously
threatened by human hunters—perhaps because few
sportsmen are willing to make the arduous climb
to the goats' mountaintop retreats.

*Nonslip pads on their hoofs enable
mountain goats to pick their way
across forbiddingly steep slopes.
Calm and deliberate, the animals
seem indifferent to dizzying heights.*

*The female mountain goat bears
one, or sometimes two, kids any
time between late April and June.
The agile youngsters can stand on
their feet within ten minutes after
birth and can jump within thirty
minutes.*

west of the Rockies' main axis. There are the Uintas, which, like the Smokies, run almost east to west; the Wasatch Range, which looks down on the valley of Great Salt Lake; and many more.

One of the most famous ranges is the Sierra Nevada, a row of tall mountains stretching along the eastern border of California. The Sierras formed as a result of *block faulting*. Essentially they are a huge block of granite that tilted upward along its eastern edge sometime in the distant past. As a result, the mountains rise gradually from west to east, but from the eastern summits the slopes drop abruptly for thousands of feet.

In the millennia since their formation, the Sierras have been endlessly sculptured by running water and glacial ice. As a result, they are filled with magnificent scenery such as the famed Yosemite Valley, a huge mountain valley carved by glaciers and hemmed in by massive rock formations. To the south lie Kings Canyon and Sequoia National Parks, famous for their groves of giant sequoias, largest of all living things. And from their bases in the arid upper Sonoran zone to their snowy, treeless summits, the Sierra Nevadas are alive with a fantastic variety of wildlife and plants.

In contrast to the Sierras, the more northerly Cascade Range is volcanic in origin. It extends from northern California across Oregon and Washington, and continues north into Canada. Lassen Peak, in California, is the only volcano in the continental United States that may still be active; it last erupted as recently as 1921. Mount Shasta stands nearby, its 14,162-foot summit rising about two miles above its base. In Oregon, Mount Hood dominates a vast forest wilderness. To the south lies Mount Mazama, whose summit cradles the deep, unbelievably blue waters of Crater Lake.

Mount Baker, Mount Adams, and still other giant peaks continue north into Canada. But all the mountains of the Washington Cascades seem insignificant compared with Mount Rainier. Many people consider this almost perfectly formed volcanic peak to be the most beautiful single moun-

Sheer glacier-carved walls, some more than half a mile
high, hem in Yosemite Valley in California's Yosemite
National Park, a preserve that embraces more than
one thousand square miles of Sierra Nevada wilderness.

tain in the country. Certainly no other American mountain dominates its surroundings so completely. Its snow-clad summit is visible from a hundred miles away in all directions, still glinting in the evening sun long after dusk has come to the lowlands. From the streets of Tacoma, forty-five miles away, the mountain seems so near that it is difficult to grasp the fact that its summit is more than fourteen thousand feet high, about eight thousand feet higher than its base. And nearly all that distance is barren of trees—just a formidable sweep of rugged rocks and permanent snowfields.

On the mountain of ice

The approach to Mount Rainier National Park passes through lush coniferous forests. The highway is lined with enormous Douglasfirs, western white pines, lodgepole pines, western hemlocks, alpine firs, and western redcedars. But once you enter the park and begin climbing Mount Rainier's base, the forest thins out rapidly. In this cool northern land, tree dwarfing and timber line appear at comparatively low elevations. At just five thousand feet above sea level, the forest already begins to give way to alpine meadows. They look much like the alpine meadows we have explored on other mountains, yet they are unique: in this case the mountain rises still another eight thousand feet. When you look up at the tremendous sweep of snowy slopes towering above, you will get the feeling that you are truly on a mountain of ice.

Many of the flowers are the same ones we saw in the Rockies, but Ranier has some striking new ones too. One of the most notable is the avalanche lily, a close relative of glacier lilies, though the blossoms are snowy white instead of yellow and have butter-yellow centers. The flowers—often five or six to a cluster—also are much larger than those of glacier lilies, and the stems are taller and the leaves much bigger. Habitat, however, is the same. Avalanche lilies grow at the margins of snowfields and icefields and continue blooming as long as melting snow exposes new ground.

Heathers also bloom profusely on Mount Rainier and other western peaks, though they are not true heathers like those found in Europe. There are both pink and white

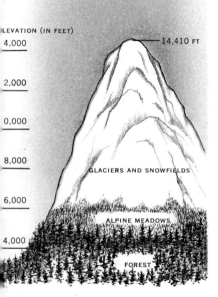

LEVATION (IN FEET)
4,000
14,410 FT
2,000
0,000
GLACIERS AND SNOWFIELDS
8,000
6,000
ALPINE MEADOWS
4,000
FOREST

Because it is a tall mountain in a northern location, much of Mount Rainier is devoid of vegetation. Timber line occurs at about five thousand feet. Beyond about six thousand feet this impressive peak is covered by glaciers and permanent snowfields.

184

Perhaps the most famous landmark of the Pacific Northwest, Mount Rainier's snow-covered 14,410-foot-high summit is visible for miles around in all directions. The massive peak, a dormant volcano that was mildly active as recently as 1870, fills about one-quarter of the 378-square-mile national park that was named for it.

High on Mount Everest in the Himalayas, intrepid climbers brave bitter temperatures and howling winds as they inch their way up rugged, ice-glazed slopes more than 25,000 feet above sea level. Yet brave men need not travel halfway around the world in search of tall mountains to test their skill, for the icy summit of our own Mount Rainier also provides a grueling challenge. The treacherous ascent of Rainier's highest slopes is so difficult, in fact, that the American team that conquered Everest in 1963 chose Mount Rainier as its training ground.

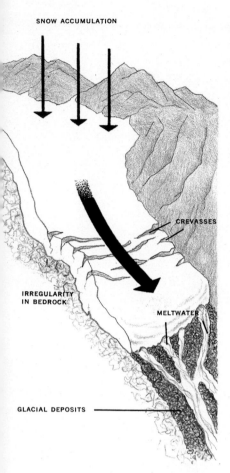

SNOW ACCUMULATION

CREVASSES

IRREGULARITY
IN BEDROCK

MELTWATER

GLACIAL DEPOSITS

The raw material of a glacier is the snow that accumulates on the upper mountain slopes. Compressed into ice, the great mass slides slowly downslope, scouring the bedrock and picking up debris as it advances. Where it slips across irregularities in the bedrock, the glacier splits open into enormous cracks called crevasses. At lower altitudes the glacier melts, giving rise to cold, tempestuous streams and depositing the debris it has eroded from the mountain slopes.

ones, just as there are both purple and white heathers in Scotland, and like European heathers they have bell-shaped flowers hanging in masses from the twigs. The heather beds, sometimes acres in extent, begin to take on color about a week or ten days after melting snow has exposed them. By the time they are in full bloom, they form brilliant masses of color on the mountainsides. Bear grass, bistort, paintbrush, lupine, and scores of other blooms nearby add to the spectacle.

Often, when the flowers are at their best, you can expect to see hummingbirds probing the blossoms with their long, slender beaks. Rufous hummingbirds breed on Mount Rainier and usually are abundant. Calliope hummingbirds also are conspicuous. Measuring only about three inches in length and weighing scarcely one-tenth of an ounce, they are among the smallest of all North American birds. Their backs are green, and the throats of the males are marked with rosettes of purple-red feathers.

The slopes of Mount Rainier harbor many other creatures as well. Here too you can find mountain goats, pikas, black bears, marmots, porcupines, and elk. Moist, wooded valleys shelter mountain beavers, small distant relatives of true beavers that are found only in the Pacific Northwest. They build extensive systems of burrows and usually venture out only after dark to feed on twigs and other plant material.

The most distinctive feature of Mount Rainier is the world of the upper slopes, the world with no life at all. Twenty-six active glaciers, some of them hundreds of feet thick, radiate from the mountain's summit. In all, they cover about forty square miles, forming the largest single-peak glacial system south of the Canadian border.

Even without climbing to the heights you can witness some effects of glaciers. Milky gray streams of silt-laden water flow from the glaciers' snouts. On summer days, when the heat of the sun increases the rate of melting, the rate of flow in the streams increases sharply in the afternoon and then subsides in the evening. A stream that seems calm in the morning is frequently transformed into a raging torrent by late afternoon, even though not a drop of rain has fallen. Some of the glaciers, such as Paradise and Winthrop Glaciers, are accessible and easy to investigate. But others are crisscrossed by deep, gaping *crevasses*,

188

enormous cracks that develop as the glacier slips across uneven terrain. These are more dangerous and best left for the expert mountain climbers who flock to icy Mount Rainier for thrills and practice climbs.

Mountains by the sea

Still farther west, fringing the Pacific from northern California to British Columbia, are the Coast Ranges, not so high as the Cascades perhaps, but still rugged and spectacular. Here, as in few places in the world, tall mountains rise abruptly from the edge of the sea itself.

The nearness of the ocean influences every facet of life on these coastal mountains. Mostly it is a matter of water. East of the mountains are great expanses of semidesert land, yet on the ocean side the mountains seem to drip with water. Winds that blow in constantly across the Pacific are heavy with moisture. But when the air currents strike the mountains, they are forced upward. As they rise, the air cools and the moisture condenses as fog or rain.

As a result, the northern portion of the Coast Ranges, around Olympic National Park, is the wettest place in the continental United States; on the average, the area receives about 140 inches of precipitation every year. The dry area beyond the mountains, in contrast, is described as lying in a *rain shadow*; by the time the winds have crossed the mountains, they have been drained of almost every drop of moisture. Farther east the winds pick up more water. But when they cross the Rockies, once again they are figuratively "squeezed dry," so that we find another rain shadow on the plains just east of the Rocky Mountains.

Thus when it is not raining along the coastal strip, the land is frequently shrouded in fog. On most days, if you see the sun at all, you glimpse it only briefly in the afternoon. In addition, ocean currents moderate the climate. It never gets really cold along the coast, but it is never really hot either. In many places in the lowlands, average temperatures in January are just about the same as those in June.

The result of this mild climate and abundant moisture is an almost tropical profusion of great trees. In this belt in northern California the giant redwoods grow, trees so huge

The Coast Ranges of the Pacific Northwest act as barriers for the warm, damp winds that blow in from the Pacific Ocean. Forced upward by the mountain slopes, the air masses cool and lose most of their moisture in the form of fog, rain, and snow. As a result, the western slopes of the Coast Ranges support lush, almost junglelike forests. The land to the east, lying within the rain shadow of the mountains, is semiarid.

The Pacific Ocean laps at the very feet of the Coast Ranges in Oregon.

that they are almost beyond belief. Sitka spruce, western hemlock, and Douglasfir also grow to enormous sizes in the coastal forests. Some of the more abundant shrubs are coast rhododendron, azalea, salal, blueberry, manzanita, and ceanothus, while forest openings are filled with beds of lupines, lilies, larkspurs, trillium, irises, paintbrushes, and poppies.

The finest of the coastal forests are found in Washington's Olympic National Park. In sheltered valleys where the Hoh, Quinault, and other rivers rush down to the sea, the forests have a lushness that seems truly junglelike. In this *temperate rain forest*, none of the trees is as large as the coast redwoods, yet many are giants of their kind. In the dim light beneath the trees, lavish growths of shrubs and waist-high ferns nearly cover the forest floor. Rain falls almost every day, and when it is not raining, the slopes are usually cloaked with mist. Water drips constantly from the leaves and trickles across the thick, cushiony mats of moss that cover most of the tree trunks. Here indeed is a forest so luxuriant that you may well imagine you have entered some lost world, perhaps in a faraway tropical wilderness.

From sea to summit

Yet if you visit the rain forest, you have explored only one face of Olympic National Park. Also in the park is our largest herd of Roosevelt elk, heaviest of the American wapiti. Mountain goats live in the park, along with mountain lions, black bears, mountain beavers, black-tailed deer, marmots, pikas, coyotes, and a host of other animals. The mountains, moreover, are big; the highest, Mount Olympus, reaches 7965 feet, almost within sight of the ocean. The mountains also are famous for their alpine meadows, their large fresh-water lakes, and their great glaciers and snow-fields in the vast wilderness above timber line.

For sheer contrast, few experiences can match a drive over Olympic's Hurricane Ridge Road. In a distance of just

Towering redwoods abound in the coastal mountains of California *(left)*; farther north is Washington's Olympic rain forest *(right)*, famous for its incredibly lush plant life. The forests in both areas benefit from the wet, mild climate provided by damp winds that blow in from the Pacific Ocean.

a few miles, this incredible highway carries you from sea level on the north side of the Olympic Peninsula to bleak snowfields beyond tree line. The entire journey requires only a half hour or so of driving time, yet the start and finish are so vastly different as to suggest that you might have traveled a thousand miles.

The beginning of the road, near Port Angeles on the coast, lies in the transition zone. On these northern Pacific shores, the transition forest is composed primarily of Douglasfir, western hemlock, western redcedar, and Sitka spruce. This dense, fragrant forest extends from sea level to heights of two to three thousand feet, where it gives way to the Pacific silver fir, western hemlock, and western white pine of the Canadian zone. The alpine fir, mountain hemlock, and Alaska yellow-cedar of the Hudsonian zone eventually become flagged and then dwarfed, and finally disappear at about five thousand feet.

Yet this leaves more than two thousand feet of the mountains still unclimbed. Vast expanses of arctic-alpine tundra sweep up the slopes before you. Because of the moist climate, they hold some of the finest alpine gardens to be seen anywhere. Most of the showier plants we have come upon before—avalanche and glacier lilies, bear grass, buttercups, bistort, heather, penstemon, larkspur, lupine, and so on. Even so, you will scarcely be prepared for their vigor and abundance in this humid, relatively mild climate.

Parking areas and overlooks are scattered at convenient intervals along the road. From some of them miles of foot trails provide easy access to the meadows, where you might glimpse a black-tailed deer followed by her fawns, sight a raven or an eagle, or discover the grassy nest of a horned lark. And all the overlooks command tremendous vistas of snow-covered peaks and forested wilderness. In a few places you can see the whole northern portion of the Olympic Peninsula, from the Strait of Juan de Fuca and Vancouver Island to the north, to the Cascade Range beyond Puget Sound to the east. Truly, Olympic is a national park beyond compare, a setting such as you might imagine could exist

Other parks may boast more spectacular scenery than Washington's Olympic National Park, but few of them offer such a wide variety of habitats. Seashore, temperate rain forest, upland coniferous forest, alpine tundra—at Olympic you can visit them all in a single day.

194

With luck, you might see mountain lion kittens in Olympic National Park—but beware, for the mother probably is nearby! The youngsters, usually born in spring, are conspicuously spotted until the age of six months, and then they take on the tawny coloration of adults.

only in a dream world. Yet it is real, and it is yours to enjoy. Its only boundaries are your own knowledge and understanding of the wonders you see.

The spell of the mountains

On our brief tour of the American mountains, we have lingered on many peaks, high and low, eastern and western, as diversified as you could wish them to be. We have journeyed to areas where we could look into Canada and others where we could catch a glimpse of Mexico. We have examined ancient mountains in the East and Middle West —just hills, really—showing all the wear that time has given them, and we have hiked to the summits of much younger mountains in the Rockies and along the Pacific Coast.

And yet the question remains, why do people climb mountains? Of course there is the classic answer, "Because they are there." But that is the alpinist's response, and we cannot all be skilled mountain climbers. Other, more com-

196

pelling reasons must account for the spell that mountains cast over so many people.

Perhaps part of their allure lies in the ease with which we can change our environment in mountain regions. If we are dissatisfied with things as they are, we can climb or descend; a few minutes and a little distance in either direction bring us to new worlds.

But another facet of the question also is worth exploring. Perhaps we climb mountains simply to see what lies beyond. Man, with his insatiable curiosity, has always sought the gaps in mountain chains, and through the passes has built his trails, caravan routes, railroads, and highways. Breaks in the continuity of mountain chains have different names in different parts of the country. In New England and upper New York they are called notches. Wilmington Notch, Smuggler's Notch, Franconia Notch, and Pinkham Notch are all scenic tourist attractions—and all are gateways in man's unending quest for the new.

Farther south, in the Appalachians, the openings are known as gaps—water gaps if a stream passes through, wind gaps if there is no flowing water. Delaware Water Gap, northeast of Philadelphia, is a notable example. So

Slightly smaller and darker than the mule deer, the aptly named black-tailed deer is a specialty of the Pacific Northwest, where it ranges from damp coastal forests to the windy summits beyond timber line.

are Cumberland Gap, Daniel Boone's old route to the West, and Newfound Gap, which carries the only road that leads across the Great Smokies.

Westerners are likely to refer to the breaks as passes, a term that somehow evokes more romance than either of the other two. For mountain men, traders, explorers, and pioneers, these were the routes west, and finding the right one could be a matter of life or death to the traveler. Donner Pass in the Sierras, for example, was named for a party of settlers who died there because they failed to cross the mountains before winter snows closed in. South Pass, the only opening for hundreds of miles in the central Rockies, was the route used by thousands of pioneers bound for California and Oregon, and by Mormons bound for their Promised Land in Utah. Glorieta Pass in New Mexico and Berthoud Pass, Loveland Pass, and Wolf Creek Pass, all in Colorado, are names that sing with the history of the West.

This, then, is the spell of the mountains. Traditionally they have caused man to look upward, to aspire, and to climb. From their slopes and summits he has seen wider horizons and gained fresh insights. And through their gateways he has found his way to new lands, new discoveries, and new adventures.

Lured upward by the spell of the heights, a team of climbers pauses at the brink of a glacial crevasse on Mount Challenger in the Cascade Range. Whether they seek adventure or a deeper understanding of alpine life, men everywhere find inspiration when they come to explore the strange and exciting world of the mountains.

Appendix

Mountains in the National Park System

Many of our finest national parks and monuments are located in mountain country. And these areas, administered by the National Park Service of the United States Department of the Interior, encompass some of the most spectacular mountain scenery to be found anywhere in North America. It is hardly surprising that the parks and monuments are visited each year by more than 100 million Americans who come to hike, camp, fish, sail, and enjoy other forms of outdoor recreation.

Yet many visitors come for more serious purposes, for the parks are something more than gigantic playgrounds. They are living museums as well. Within their borders are preserved some of the few remaining areas of the primeval American landscape as it appeared before the arrival of the first colonists. With the help of interpretive centers, marked nature trails, and programs conducted by skilled ranger-naturalists, the Park Service guides visitors to a fuller understanding of the forces that have shaped the landscape, of the relationships of plants and animals to each other and to the land where they live, and of man's own place in the natural world.

Whether he wishes to observe how mountains are formed or to learn of the ways in which plants and wildlife are adapted for survival in mountain country, the visitor is sure to find both knowledge and inspiration in our country's far-flung National Park System. Notable features of some of the mountainous parks and monuments are described below.

Acadia National Park (Maine)

Located on the rugged New England coast, Acadia is the only national park in the northeastern United States. Most of the park lies on Mount Desert Island, the eroded remnant of a highland that once stood far inland but is now exposed to the tides. The island is covered with gently rounded mountains that were sculptured by advancing glaciers during the ice age. The tallest peak in the park, Cadillac Mountain, is 1530 feet high. Land meets sea in Acadia, and its plants and animals are at once those of northern forests and the seashore.

Big Bend National Park (Texas)

Big Bend is a park of contrasts: cool mountain forests of Douglasfir, ponderosa pine, and other conifers grow at higher elevations in the rugged Chisos Mountains; cholla, giant dagger, prickly pear, ocotillo, and other desert plants thrive on the lower slopes and in arid bottom lands. Among the most interesting animals here are the rare Colima warbler, which is not known to nest anywhere else north of the Mexican border; the collared

GIANT DAGGER

peccary, North America's only native wild pig; and the ringtail, a shy nocturnal prowler with a strikingly banded tail.

Blue Ridge Parkway *(Virginia and North Carolina)*

The Blue Ridge Parkway is a 469-mile-long scenic highway connecting Virginia's Shenandoah National Park and the Great Smoky Mountains National Park in North Carolina and Tennessee. Throughout its length the parkway follows the contours of the Blue Ridge Mountains and other ranges. Because of the relatively high altitudes, many typically northern plants and animals are able to extend their ranges south along the mountain chains. In addition to fine scenery, the parkway is famous for its wild flowers, especially the spectacle of azaleas, rhododendrons, and mountain laurel that bloom at various altitudes from early spring to late July.

Chiricahua National Monument *(Arizona)*

This monument in the Chiricahua Mountains was set aside primarily to preserve a seventeen-square-mile area of fantastically eroded rock formations. Great expanses of pinnacles, balanced rocks, spires, turrets, and other weird formations create a truly unearthly scene. In addition, the cooler climate in the mountains makes them a haven for many unexpected plants and animals in an arid semidesert countryside. Cool north-facing slopes are covered with Arizona cypresses, scrub oaks, manzanitas, and madroñas, while warmer south-facing slopes harbor such desert species as yuccas, century plants, and cactuses. The most frequently sighted large mammal is the Arizona white-tailed deer, but collared peccaries and ringtails also are seen occasionally.

CLARK'S NUTCRACKER

Crater Lake National Park *(Oregon)*

The chief attraction here is a deep, blue lake filling the crater of an extinct volcano. The lower slopes of this famous peak in the Cascade Range are forested with ponderosa pine, Douglasfir, and sugar pine; Shasta fir, subalpine fir, mountain hemlock, and other trees grow around the edge of the lake. On the rim, listen for the harsh call of the Clark's nutcracker, one of the commonest of the 160 birds that have been observed in the park. Golden-mantled ground squirrels, pikas, red foxes, and black bears are a few of the park's more conspicuous mammal residents.

Craters of the Moon National Monument *(Idaho)*

This spectacular area of lava flows, cinder cones, and other formations is the product of eons of intense volcanic activity. One of the most impressive formations, Big Cinder Butte, is the largest cinder cone of its kind in the world; its 800-foot-high mass of debris was formed when molten lava was thrown into the air, cooled rapidly, and then fell as frothy cinders in a symmetrical circle around the escape vent. Other products of volcanic activity, such as tree molds, pit craters, lava bombs, lava tubes, and many more, contribute to the eerie fascination of the monument's moonlike landscape.

Death Valley National Monument (California and Nevada)

This rugged 140-mile-long valley between the Panamint and Amargosa Ranges is a place of startling contrasts. Since elevations range from 282 feet below sea level (the lowest point in North America) to 11,049 feet above sea level, the park displays a wide range of climatic conditions. Fine stands of foxtail and pinyon pines are found at high elevations, while lush groves of cottonwoods and willows flourish in well-watered canyons at lower elevations. In years when rainfall is sufficient, wild flowers bloom everywhere—astragalus, evening primroses, phacelias, eriogonums, poppies, and many more. The rare desert bighorn is present, but difficult to find.

Glacier Bay National Monument (Alaska)

This unique preserve on the Alaska panhandle is an ideal place for viewing active glaciers. The bay itself nestles between two of the loftiest mountain ranges in the United States, the Fairweather Range and the Saint Elias Range, which is dominated by 18,000-foot Mount Saint Elias. Many active glaciers on the mountains end in sheer ice walls, from which huge chunks of ice periodically fall into the water in the bay. Especially intriguing are the areas where retreating glaciers are being replaced by hardy pioneer plants and mature forests. The moss-draped forests of spruce and hemlock on lower slopes are inhabited by grizzly, brown, and black bears as well as martens, red foxes, and mink.

MARTEN

Glacier National Park (Montana)

Glacier is unique in that it is the only park in the world to cross an international border; together with Canada's Waterton Lakes National Park it forms Waterton-Glacier International Peace Park. The entire area, famous as a showcase for past glacial activity, is a hiker's paradise. A thousand miles of trails wind through the mountains and lead visitors to remote valleys where they can expect to see mountain goats and even a few small but still slightly active glaciers. Mount Cleveland, at 10,438 feet, is the highest peak in the mountain chain that angles across the park.

Grand Teton National Park (Wyoming)

The rugged Grand Tetons are a perfect example of fault-block mountains; they were formed as a great block of the earth's surface moved slowly upward along a crack, or fault, in the earth's crust. Erosion by wind, water, and ice later sculptured the angular contours of the range, which rises abruptly for more than

205

7000 feet above the valley floor at Jackson Hole. Grand Teton (13,766 feet) is the highest peak in the park, and many others exceed 12,000 feet, making the Grand Tetons especially popular with mountain climbers. The extensive lowland areas are dotted with lakes and covered with coniferous forests, which harbor elks, moose, trumpeter swans, and a host of other animals.

Great Smoky Mountains National Park
(North Carolina and Tennessee)

These ancient folded mountains are the eroded remnants of a range that probably stood much taller in the distant past. Even so, many of the peaks still reach well above six thousand feet. Because of their southern location, however, none of the mountains surpasses timber line. About six hundred miles of trails lead through dense cove forests, across open balds, and to the highest summits of this primeval wilderness. Long a favorite with campers and hikers, the Great Smokies also are a haven for botanists; the area boasts more plant species than any other park in the country, including gigantic specimens of trees such as yellow buckeyes, eastern hemlocks, and silver-bell trees.

Guadalupe Mountains National Park (Texas)

This relatively new and still essentially undeveloped national park stands where two great mountain ranges merge in a scenic wilderness of high peaks and steep-walled canyons. In this arid region, permanent streams in the canyons support lush oases of walnut, chinquapin oak, madroñas, and other broadleaf trees, while the taller peaks are forested with ponderosa pines. On cooler slopes, Douglasfir and aspen forests provide refuge for elk, mule deer, bears, and a few mountain lions. Watch also for wild turkeys and, at night, porcupines.

Haleakala National Park (Island of Maui, Hawaii)

A monument to volcanic activity on a grand scale, most of this dramatic park (pronounced *hah*-lay-*ah*-kah-lah) lies within the gigantic crater of a dormant volcano. The rim of the crater stands 10,023 feet above sea level, while the floor of the 3000-foot-deep basinlike crater is dotted with huge cinder cones, some of them 1000 feet high. Here, high above sea level, live such rare species as the nene, or Hawaiian goose, and the silversword, a strange plant that grows only on the islands of Maui and Hawaii. Thirty miles of trails lead to major points of interest in the park.

Hawaii Volcanoes National Park (Island of Hawaii, Hawaii)

The major features of this park are two of the most active volcanoes in the world, Mauna Loa and Kilauea. Both still come to life from time to time, and any visitor can hope that he will be lucky enough to witness one of the wild eruptions; the most

DOUGLASFIR

CONE

206

recent ones occurred in the mid-1960s. When the volcanoes are dormant, the park offers plenty of other attractions. The famous fern forest on the mountain slopes is filled with incredibly colorful native birds—apapanes, amakihis, iiwis, and many others.

Katmai National Monument (Alaska)
Famed for its Valley of the Ten Thousand Smokes, Katmai is an area of ocean bays and lagoons, glacier-carved mountains, active volcanoes, and lush forests of white spruce. Much of the grandeur of its scenery resulted from a great eruption of Novarupta Volcano on June 6, 1912, when two and one-half cubic miles of volcanic ash and rock fragments were sent flying into the air and then filled the valley with debris to depths of seven hundred feet. Several volcanoes still produce smoke, and one occasionally sends out streams of lava. The monument's most notable resident mammal is the Alaska brown bear, the largest land carnivore in North America.

Lassen Volcanic National Park (California)
Boiling mudholes, hissing steam vents, cinder cones, lava flows, and other evidence of volcanic activity abound throughout this showplace for studying the results of volcanism. The park's central attraction is 10,457-foot Lassen Peak, a volcano that was active as recently as 1917. In addition, more than seven hundred varieties of plants grow in the park. Lush coniferous forests blanket the lowlands, and lupines, penstemons, paintbrushes, and other wild flowers provide a continuing spectacle of blossoms from June until late September. Beavers, bears, pikas, porcupines, martens, jays, and other animals flourish throughout the park, and the lakes and streams are filled with rainbow, brook, and brown trout and other fish.

MOOSE

Mount McKinley National Park (Alaska)
This park, located just 250 miles south of the Arctic Circle, is dominated by 20,320-foot-high Mount McKinley, the tallest peak in North America. Although most of the peak itself is covered by glaciers and permanent snowfields, broad valleys at lower elevations are heavily forested. Wildlife is plentiful, especially on the tundra, but most visitors are particularly interested in sighting grizzly bears, caribou, Dall's sheep, wolves, and moose. Set off on a backpacking trip and chances are good that you will pass through areas that have never before been seen by humans.

Mount Rainier National Park (Washington)
Mount Rainier, a dormant volcano in the Cascade Range, rises to a height of 14,410 feet. From its summit downward, glaciers and huge snowfields grade into broad alpine meadows, which in turn give way to forests of fir and pine, and then, at low elevations,

Douglasfir, western hemlock, and western redcedar. The largest of the twenty-six active glaciers in the park is Emmons Glacier, covering an area five miles long and a mile wide. Rainier's upper slopes provide excellent sport for experienced mountain climbers; for the less adventurous, its alpine meadows offer spectacular displays of colorful wild flowers.

Olympic National Park (Washington)

This picturesque area is really three parks in one: along the park's narrow coastal strip, dramatic rocky beaches overlook the Pacific Ocean; sheltered valleys on the lower mountain slopes are cloaked with dense rain forests of 300-foot-tall Sitka spruces, western hemlocks, Douglasfirs, and other moss-draped trees; finally, the windswept summit of Mount Olympus (7965 feet) is a rugged wilderness of glaciers and alpine tundra. Whether you seek a glimpse of shore birds along the coast or the herds of Roosevelt elk that winter in the rain forest, more than six hundred miles of trails will help you find your way to most of the points of interest in the park.

Pinnacles National Monument (California)

The pinnacles are remnants of an ancient volcano that have been shaped by wind, rain, heat, and frost into sharply pointed spires rising high above California's chaparral country. Here—where summer temperatures usually reach one hundred degrees by midday—grow leathery-leaved shrubs such as greasewood chamise, manzanita, buckbrush ceanothus, and hollyleaf cherry. These chaparral plants provide food and shelter for a wide variety of animals, among them black-tailed deer, gray foxes, bobcats, California quail, and turkey vultures.

Rocky Mountain National Park (Colorado)

This superb mountain park, in one of the most scenic areas of the Rocky Mountains, embraces more than 100 peaks, including 17 between 13,000 and 14,000 feet high and another 44 over 12,000 feet. On the lower mountain slopes are open, parklike stands of ponderosa pine, which grade upward into dense forests of spruce and fir. Broad expanses of alpine tundra are readily accessible by automobile; several of the peaks are traversed by Trail Ridge Road, the highest continuous road in the United States. Rocky Mountain bighorns, elk, beavers, and ptarmigans are just a few of the park's wildlife species.

Sequoia and Kings Canyon National Parks (California)

These great parks in the Sierra Nevadas are studded with tall peaks, but the most majestic is the 14,495-foot summit of Mount Whitney in Sequoia National Park, the highest point in the

FEMALE

MALE

CALIFORNIA QUAIL

United States south of Alaska. Many overlooks along roads in the parks provide fine views of the scenery, but the best vistas are seen by those who hike into more remote wilderness areas. Nearly a thousand lakes, deep glacier-carved canyons, broad alpine meadows, and lush forests all contribute to the parks' variety, but their most noted features are groves of sequoias, the largest in bulk of all living things.

Shenandoah National Park (Virginia)

The park's central feature is the Skyline Drive, a scenic highway that winds for 105 miles along the crest of the Blue Ridge Mountains. Along the way it passes more than sixty peaks from three thousand to over four thousand feet high. Spectacular panoramas of misty mountains and broad valleys greet the motorist at every turn in the road, while hiking trails tempt him to investigate the park's sheltered coves, rushing mountain streams, and lush forests of oaks, hickories, maples, locusts, hemlocks, and other trees. Ideal times for a visit are late autumn, when the hills are ablaze with color, and late spring, when the forests are filled with flowering shrubs and woodland wild flowers.

Yellowstone National Park (Wyoming, Montana, Idaho)

Yellowstone, the largest national park in the United States, is a mountain area that offers something for everyone. For the casual sightseer there are the famous geysers, mineral pools, and other thermal features. Then too there are Yellowstone Lake and the Grand Canyon of the Yellowstone River with its beautiful waterfalls. But to many people, the park's greatest attraction is its hundreds of square miles of mountain wilderness, where many peaks in the Absaroka Mountains have elevations of ten thousand to more than eleven thousand feet. Hike through the backcountry, and chances are good that you will glimpse black bears, moose, elk, pronghorns, bison, white pelicans, trumpeter swans, dippers, and a host of other wild creatures.

Yosemite National Park (California)

The most heavily visited area of this park in the Sierra Nevadas is the beautiful glacier-carved gorge of Yosemite Valley, famed for its sheer walls, its towering rock formations such as Half Dome and El Capitan, and the plumelike Upper and Lower Yosemite Falls, which spill for a combined total of 2425 feet down the face of one of the cliffs. Nearby are three groves of giant sequoia trees. In sharp contrast are the park's vast areas of rugged mountain country, with lofty peaks, broad alpine meadows, and scores of lakes and streams. Because of the great variation in elevation, life zones in the park range from upper Sonoran to arctic-alpine.

BLACK LOCUST

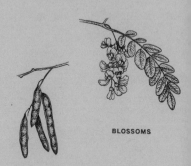

BLOSSOMS

SEED PODS

Vanishing Wildlife of the Mountains

In the early 1960s, the United States Department of the Interior established a special committee to investigate the alarming decline in populations of many species of North American wildlife. The committee's preliminary report listed forty kinds of birds and mammals that have fallen into extinction over the past 150 years. More than half of them have disappeared from the face of the earth since 1900.

Worse still, the scientists' findings indicated that an even greater number of species are faced with the prospect of extinction in the near future. Only immediate legal protection and vigorous action to promote their increase can offer these endangered animals the slightest prospect for survival.

Man, of course, has not been directly responsible for the extinction of every species that has been lost from our continent.

NENE, OR HAWAIIAN GOOSE
When white men first set foot on the Hawaiian Islands, thousands of nene (pronounced nay-nay) flourished on the volcanic mountain slopes. But so many of the big geese were slaughtered and shipped to California to feed hungry forty-niners that, by the time the hunting was banned in 1911, less than fifty remained. More recently, efforts to raise the birds in captivity and return them to the wild have proved successful. Although still dangerously rare, some three hundred of Hawaii's state birds now live on the islands, principally in Haleakala National Park.

GRIZZLY BEAR
Although grizzly bears are fairly plentiful in Alaska, only about five hundred remain in Canada and another eight hundred or so live in the northern Rockies, principally in Yellowstone and Glacier National Parks. The bears' greatest enemy is human ignorance; for centuries, hunters have been slaughtering grizzlies on sight. Equally damaging has been the constant shrinkage of the large wilderness tracts required by the bears. The only means of assuring this legendary beast's survival is to preserve wild areas and restrict hunting, trapping, and poisoning throughout its range.

Like the dinosaurs, thousands of species disappeared from the earth long before the appearance of man. But for the vast majority of animals that are presently faced with extinction, a major threat to survival is man's abuse of the natural world. When a wild animal's habits seem to conflict with human interests, many people are tempted to exterminate the species. In order to provide for the needs of a burgeoning human population, civilization nibbles ceaselessly at the borders of the remaining islands of wilderness. In the name of progress, we drain marshes, cut down entire forests, spread poisonous chemicals across the land, and in many other ways destroy or seriously damage wildlife habitat. Almost all forms of life suffer as a result.

This trend can be reversed, but only when the public has been awakened to the hazards that threaten our wildlife. Only when people have been made aware of the interdependence of all forms of life can we hope to correct the sad results of our ecological ignorance in the past. The four mountain animals pictured here are species whose prospects for survival are especially dim.

MOUNTAIN LION
Man and mountain lions apparently do not mix. Although the great cats feed mainly on weak deer and other game animals, occasional attacks on livestock seem cause enough for some men to persecute the handsome predators to extinction. Encroachment on their wilderness retreats also contributes to the lions' decline. Estimates of mountain lion populations in the United States, excluding Alaska, run from a low of 800 to a high of 6500; most of the animals live in the Pacific Northwest. Substantially larger populations survive in Canada and Alaska.

CALIFORNIA CONDOR
The entire world's population of North America's largest soaring bird—in all, about forty individuals—lives in Sespe National Condor Sanctuary in Los Padres National Forest, just seventy miles from Los Angeles. Their numbers have been on the wane since the ice age, perhaps because each pair rears just one young bird every two years. Worse still, the birds abandon their nests at the slightest disturbance, and so conservationists are vigorously opposed to any road building or recreational development in the vicinity of the birds' last retreat.

Basics of Backpacking

One of the best ways to explore mountain country is to travel on foot. You can set your own pace and linger as long as you wish at points of interest. Moreover, hiking is as easy or as difficult as you care to make it. Although some trails call for great stamina, many others are as gentle and inviting as country lanes. As a result, more and more Americans, both young and old, are discovering the pleasures of hiking.

Some of them are not content to spend just one day at a time on the trail. Instead they are learning the ways of backpacking. By carrying food, shelter, and all other necessities in packs on their backs, they are able to spend days or even weeks of vacation time on the trail.

Where to go and how to begin

When it comes to selecting a route, the backpacker is faced with almost unlimited opportunities. In all, some 105,000 miles of mountain trails wind through national forests in all areas of the country, and another 80,000 miles of trails lead to points of interest in the National Park System. Many state parks include fine hiking trails, and still other routes are maintained by private organizations. The Appalachian Trail Conference, for example, established and cares for the 2000-mile-long Appalachian Trail from Maine to Georgia. Its western counterpart, the Pacific Crest Trail, extends from the Cascades in Washington south through the Sierra Nevadas and on to Mexico.

Wherever you live, experienced hikers are certain to prove to be your best source of information on routes and techniques. Hiking clubs with hundreds of members have been established in many parts of the country. Some of the larger organizations interested in wilderness backpacking are listed in the margin. By joining a club, you can meet many enthusiasts who are eager to advise beginners on procedures and equipment. The clubs also can provide you with maps, guidebooks, and other useful publications.

Personnel at national forests and parks are always happy to furnish information on trails and other facilities in the areas they administer. In addition, the departments of conservation in most states publish magazines and brochures that offer useful hints and descriptions of trails.

Representative Hiking Clubs

Adirondack Mountain Club
  Gabriels, New York
Appalachian Mountain Club
  5 Joy Street
  Boston, Massachusetts
Appalachian Trail Conference
  1916 Sunderland Place, N.W.
  Washington, D.C.
Green Mountain Club
  108 Merchants Row
  Rutland, Vermont
Federation of Western Outdoor Clubs
  201 S. Ashdale Street
  West Covina, California
Mazamas
  909 N.W. 19 Avenue
  Portland, Oregon
The Sierra Club
  Mills Tower Building
  San Francisco, California
Wilderness Society
  2144 P Street, N.W.
  Washington, D.C.

212

Traveling light

A backpacker is like a turtle: he carries his home on his back. Food, clothing, shelter, sleeping gear, and everything else he needs for wilderness living are stowed in his backpack.

Weight, of course, is a primary consideration. Forty to fifty pounds is usually the maximum an adult male can carry comfortably; adult females generally limit their packs to thirty-five pounds. The best pack size for any individual, however, will vary with factors such as his age and physical condition, the length of the proposed trip, and the roughness of the terrain.

Most beginners try to carry too much gear. With a little experience you will find that many things are not necessary and you will discover ways to cut down on weight. For example, you soon will realize that plastic containers, besides being unbreakable, are far lighter than glass jars. You will also find that it is useful to prepare a check list of basic necessities. By going over the list before leaving on a trip, you will be certain you have not forgotten anything.

Backpacks themselves are available in a number of styles. Many people are content with the inexpensive army packs sold in surplus stores. Others prefer the type mounted on a lightweight metal frame that fits the contours of the body. In any case, be sure to choose a pack that has outside pockets where you can store smaller items you might need during the day.

BACKPACK

On the trail

Proper footgear is as important to a backpacker as is a lightweight load. If you expect to hike several miles per day, your shoes must be comfortable. Select boots or sturdy shoes with nonslip soles, and be sure they are well broken in before you begin your trip. Do not attempt to travel in cowboy boots, ski boots, or other specialized footgear. Wear two pairs of socks— heavier woolen socks over lightweight inner ones. A pair of moccasins or other comfortable shoes will provide welcome relief at the end of a day's hike.

You will find that hiking is a good deal less tiring if you travel at a steady pace. But be sure that your speed is comfortable for the slowest member of your party, and pause from time to time for short standing rests.

Before setting out, tell a forest ranger or some other responsible person where you are going and how long you expect to be gone. Study a map of the country you will be exploring and then pack the map, along with a compass, in a waterproof case. It is a good idea to pinpoint your location on the map at each rest stop. With a little practice, you soon will be able to orient yourself in terms of mountain peaks, streams, and other topographical features.

MAP AND COMPASS

213

If you should get lost, don't panic. Begin by backtracking; clues such as broken twigs, footprints, and so on probably will lead you back to familiar territory. A view of the landscape from a high vantage point may also be sufficient to orient you. Or you can follow a stream; it is certain to lead eventually to recognizable landmarks.

If you become hopelessly bewildered, don't waste energy by hiking aimlessly through the woods. Instead, build a small fire and feed it with green boughs in order to make dense smoke. Someone is certain to notice the smoke and check on its cause.

Setting up camp

Be sensible in selecting a campsite. Rolling out your sleeping bag under an open sky may sound romantic, but waking up in a sudden downpour or a freak blizzard is no fun. By the same token, a spot beside a stream may look like a good place to camp, but in a storm it could flood. It is far better to select a site on high level ground, preferably where there is some shelter from the weather and where the morning sun will warm you and dry the dew from your tent. Be sure water and fuel are available nearby.

Fortunately for the backpacker, a good selection of lightweight camping equipment is available at most sporting goods stores. In addition to air mattresses and lightweight but warm sleeping bags, you can buy tents designed especially for backpackers. They are made of lightweight fabrics such as rayon and dacron, and come complete with lightweight metal stakes and tent poles.

Many campers do not use a tent at all, but prefer to rig up a simple shelter from a large nylon or plastic ground cloth. With a length of nylon rope, the cloth can be arranged in a number of ways to accommodate as many as four people for sleeping or to provide shelter in bad weather while you prepare and eat your meals.

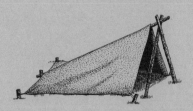

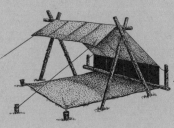

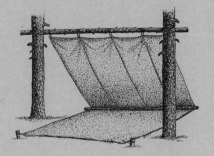

The hiker's menu

The best cooking kit for a backpacker is a set of aluminum utensils that nest one inside another. The kit should include pans for both cooking and eating. A large tin can may also prove useful as an extra pot.

As for food, every backpacker has his own preferences. Most hikers can get along on about one and a half pounds of food per day. When you plan your trip, be sure to vary your menus. More important, shop around for concentrated and dehydrated foods that will lighten your pack. Powdered soups and potatoes, dried fruit, bouillon cubes, and instant puddings, cocoa, tea, and coffee are available at almost any grocery store. In addition, stores catering to campers sell dehydrated stews, meats, and other more elaborate dishes that will take up little room in your pack.

For building a simple fireplace, a small grate from an oven will prove invaluable. Cooking over glowing embers rather than a blazing fire, besides permitting better control over temperatures, will result in far less soot on your cooking utensils.

Littering, of course, is unpardonable. Burn all papers and plastic wrappers. Tin cans can be flattened and then buried unobtrusively near your campsite. Jars and large plastic containers, on the other hand, simply will not rot. Carry them with you and dispose of them at the end of your trip. Remember the backpacker's motto: "If you carried it in, you can carry it out."

Tips for wilderness living

Living out of doors can be a rewarding experience, but only if you are prepared to cope with unfamiliar conditions. Although the air is clear and cool at high altitudes, sunburn can be a real hazard; keep covered and use suntan lotion. In some areas, flies, mosquitoes, and other insects are a nuisance; carry a bottle or stick of insect repellent. During thunderstorms keep away from lone trees and avoid exposed ridges and peaks; if you should get caught in the open, keep low.

Finally, there is always the possibility of injury. Carry a first-aid kit containing at least such basics as antiseptic, aspirin, Band-Aids, and an elastic bandage. Know the techniques of basic first aid, but seek professional assistance for more serious injury. If you have to hike out for help, leave at least one member of your party with the patient. Or you can summon aid by using the universal distress signal of three alarms, such as three shouts, three whistles, three flashes of light, or three puffs of smoke from your fire.

The Bare Necessities

Pack
Tent or ground cloth
Sleeping bag
Air mattress
Clothing:
    hiking shoes
    camp shoes
    two changes of trousers
    long-sleeved shirts
    wool shirt or sweater
    socks and underwear
    parka
    raingear
    handkerchiefs
Cooking and eating utensils
Canteen
Food: 1½ pounds per person
    per day
Flashlight with spare batteries
    and bulbs
Compass
Map and map case
First-aid kit
Suntan lotion
Insect repellent
Sunglasses
Nylon rope
Ax or hatchet
Jackknife
Matches in waterproof container
Wax candle, for lighting damp
    wood
Washing soap and towel
Soap pads
Toothbrush and toothpaste
Toilet tissue
Needles and thread
Safety pins
Trowel
Pliers

A Guide to Common Fossils

A fossil is any evidence of the existence of living things in the past, whether the evidence is simply a footprint, the outline of a seashell, or the complete skeleton of a dinosaur. The oldest known fossils on earth, the remains of primitive one-celled plants, are estimated to be more than 2 billion years old. Yet fossils are not really plentiful in rocks more than 600 million years old, mainly because most of the older rocks have been so severely altered by geological processes that the fossils in them have been destroyed.

In younger rocks the fossil record is fairly complete and has enabled scientists to gather a great deal of information about the history of the earth. Fossils, for example, provide clues about climates in the past, the former locations of seas and shorelines, and the occurrences of ancient mountain-building episodes. Just as important, they yield invaluable information about the origins and evolution of life on earth. By examining series of related fossils from progressively younger rocks, scientists are able to reconstruct the development of a particular species, such as the horse, into its present form.

Once it has been buried—whether by a lava flow, a moving sand dune, the build-up of sediments at the bottom of a body of water, or some other process—an organism can become a fossil in several ways. Petrified wood and most fossil bones, for instance, are results of petrifaction: all the hollow spaces, even in individual cells, have been filled by dissolved minerals in water that seeped through the buried organism. In other cases, almost all the material in a once living plant or animal has disappeared, leaving only a carbon tracing of the organism's form; plants, the soft parts of fish, and soft-bodied animals often are preserved in this way. Frequently the entire organism is dissolved away and the resulting hollow is filled by a cast, like plaster poured into a mold. Or, as in the case of a woolly mammoth found frozen in Siberia, the complete animal might be preserved.

In most areas, the best places to hunt for fossils are layers of shale, sandstone, or limestone that have been exposed by erosion or the works of man. Natural outcrops, roadcuts, and quarries usually are excellent fossil sites. To get started on the fascinating hobby of collecting fossils, you need only a pair of sharp eyes and a few pieces of simple equipment such as a geologist's or a bricklayer's hammer, a small chisel, and a hand lens. Your collection will be far more valuable if you record exactly where and in what rock formation each fossil was found. Pictured here are a few of the kinds of fossils you can expect to find in various areas of North America.

POCKET MAGNIFYING GLASS

CHISEL

GEOLOGIST'S HAMMER

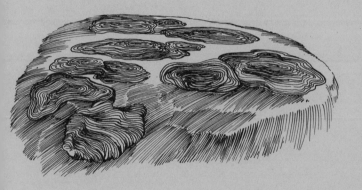

CALCAREOUS ALGAE sometimes grew in globular colonies, enlarging as new layers of microscopic plants were added on the outside. Among the most ancient of all plants, some fossil colonies are estimated to be over two billion years old. Some, like these, have been exposed in cross section by the shearing action of glaciers.

SEED FERNS, the oldest and most primitive seed-bearing plants, first appear as fossils in rocks that are about 350 million years old. Although all members of the group are now extinct, they are believed to have been the ancestors of more modern seed-bearing plants.

PETRIFIED WOOD forms spectacular displays at Petrified Forest National Monument and Yellowstone National Park, where entire fossil forests are preserved. The fossils formed as dissolved minerals gradually replaced the cells of the once living trees and literally turned them to stone.

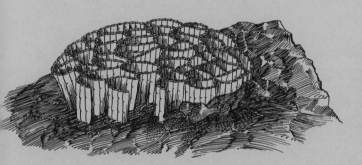

CORALS are minute marine animals that live at the surface of deposits of calcium carbonate secreted by the animals. Deposits formed by each species are distinctive. This chain coral was a widespread reef builder that lived in warm shallow seas some 415 million years ago.

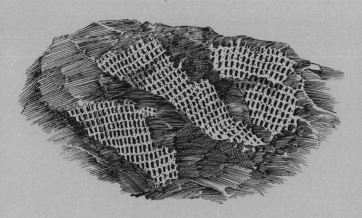

BRYOZOANS, or "moss animals," live in elaborate colonies attached to rocks and seaweeds in coastal waters. Each individual, no larger than a pencil point, lives in a tube of calcium carbonate. Bryozoan fossils are found in limestone from nearly all geological periods.

BRACHIOPODS, small marine animals still living today, are found throughout the fossil record. Each animal's body rests at the top of a stalk and is enclosed in a pair of shells of unequal size. The two halves of each shell, however, are mirror images of each other.

PELECYPODS, or clams, have been fairly common as fossils for the past 475 million years. Each animal is enclosed by identical shells on each side of its body. Unlike the shells of brachiopods, however, these are lopsided in appearance.

GASTROPODS, or snails, characterized by distinctively spiraled shells, still are common both on land and in water. Although the earliest land snail fossils have been found in hollow stumps of 300-million-year-old fossil trees, fossils of many marine forms are much older.

AMMONITES are ancient cephalopods whose best known living survivor is the chambered nautilus. As ammonites grew, they periodically moved forward in their coiled shells and sealed off the vacant chambers with pearly walls. The pattern of lines where these partitions join the outer shell helps identify fossil species.

TRILOBITES, ancient forerunners of insects and their kin, are named for the three lobes running the length of their bodies. Among the most common of all marine animals at one time, they became extinct about the time that the Appalachians were forming.

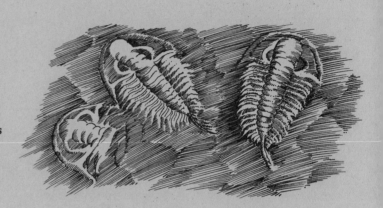

INSECTS first appeared in dense forests that flourished more than 280 million years ago. These more modern forms were preserved on the bed of an ancient lake near Florissant, Colorado, in the Rocky Mountain foothills. They were buried some 36 million years ago, at about the time when modern flowering plants were evolving.

CRINOIDS, whose tentacled bodies stand at the top of long stems, sometimes are called sea lilies; actually these still living animals are closely related to starfish. Their fragmented remains are present from the very beginning of the fossil record but are most abundant in limestone formed about 325 million years ago.

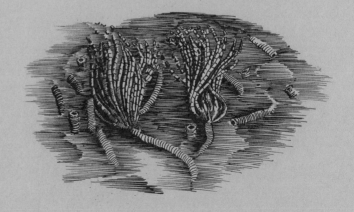

GRAPTOLITES, strange marine animals, are plentiful as fossils in dark shales throughout the world. Now extinct, they reached their peak in abundance 425 to 500 million years ago. Fragmentary remains in the rocks provide the basis for reconstructions of their colonies.

SHARK'S TEETH are practically the only remains of these ancient fish that are ever preserved as fossils, since their skeletons are formed of cartilage rather than bone. Some fossil shark's teeth are as much as six inches long, indicating the existence of real giants in the past.

FISHES first appeared as fossils some 450 million years ago, when their bodies were armored with bony plates. More modern fossils, such as this 50-million-year-old specimen, have been found in shale deposits in mountainous southwestern Wyoming and many other places.

DINOSAUR TRACKS and other trails preserved on the surface of ancient mudflats reveal a great deal about life of the past. By studying such fossils, scientists not only can identify the maker of the tracks, but can even determine whether the animal walked on two feet or four.

Adaptation: An inherited structural, functional, or behavioral characteristic that improves an organism's chances for survival in a particular *habitat. See also* Specialization.

Alpine: Pertaining to high *mountain* places. In *ecology*, the term refers to the area above *timber line. See also* Tundra.

Arctic: At or near the North Pole; pertaining to the north polar region.

Arctic-alpine zone: A *life zone* characterized by *tundra* vegetation. The zone, as proposed by C. Hart Merriam, is located above *timber line* on *mountains* and north of *Hudsonian-zone* forests in Canada and Alaska.

Arctic tundra: *See* Tundra.

Austroriparian zone: An eastern subdivision of the *lower austral zone* in C. Hart Merriam's system of *life zones.*

Bald: An open, treeless area in a *mountain* forest, especially in the southeastern United States. For unknown reasons, balds remain covered with grasses and low *shrubs* instead of growing up in trees. *See also* Heath bald.

Biome: A unit for the ecological classification of broad geographical areas. Biomes are large in extent and include all the plants and animals characteristically found living together in the area. North American biomes include such subdivisions as *desert, grass-*

land, and *coniferous forest. See also* Life zones.

Block faulting: A geologic process in which a large block of rock on the earth's crust shifts up or down in relation to the surrounding rocks. Block faulting sometimes contributes to the formation of large *mountain* ranges.

Bog: A wet, low area, often an old lake bed, filling or filled with partially decayed matter known as *peat.*

Boreal: Northern; of a northern character.

Canadian zone: A *life zone,* proposed by C. Hart Merriam, with lower average temperatures than those of the *transition zone* and higher average temperatures than those of the *Hudsonian zone.* The Canadian zone is typically forested with northern coniferous trees, which are usually intermixed with willows and aspens.

Canyon: A deep, steep-sided valley eroded into the land by the running water of a stream or river.

Carolinian zone: An eastern subdivision of the *upper austral zone* in C. Hart Merriam's classification of *life zones.*

Catkin: A tassellike cluster of small flowers that grows on willows, birches, and certain other trees.

Circumpolar: Surrounding one of the poles. A plant or animal *species* that lives in high-*latitude* land areas throughout the Northern or Southern Hemisphere is said to have a circumpolar distribution.

Climate: The average weather conditions of an area, including temperature, rainfall, humidity, wind, and hours of sunlight, based on records kept for many years.

Competition: The struggle between individuals or groups of living things for such common necessities as food or living space.

Conifer: A plant that bears its seeds in cones. The term usually refers to needle-leaf trees such as pine, spruce, and fir, although some coniferous *species*, such as yew and juniper, bear fruits that look like berries rather than cones.

Coniferous forest: A transcontinental *biome* in which the predominant vegetation is coniferous trees. Coniferous forests are found across most of Canada but also extend south into the United States along high *mountain* ranges.

Conservation: The use of natural resources in a way that ensures their continuing availability to future generations; the wise use of natural resources.

Cove: A sheltered recess at the foot of a steep *mountain* slope. In the southern Appalachian Mountains, the rich, well-watered soil in coves supports forests that are notable for the variety and large size of their trees.

Crevasse: A deep crack or uneven opening in the surface of a *glacier*, formed when the glacier slips over uneven terrain.

Deciduous: Describing a plant that periodically loses all its leaves, usually in autumn. Most North American broadleaf trees are deciduous. A few *conifers*, such as tamarack and cypress, also are deciduous. *See also* Evergreen.

Deciduous forest: A *biome* that includes most of the eastern United States, where the predominant vegetation is *deciduous* trees.

Desert: An unforested *biome* where rainfall is slight or unevenly distributed throughout the year. Daytime temperatures in deserts usually are high, and vegetation is sparse.

Ecology: The scientific study of the relationships of living things to one another and to their *environment*. A scientist who studies these relationships is an ecologist.

Edge effect: The tendency for plant and animal populations to be denser and more varied in areas where two distinctive *habitats* meet and intermingle than they are in either of the separate habitats.

Encinal: A type of forest, composed primarily of stunted *evergreen* oaks, widespread on high *mountain* slopes of Mexico's Sierra Madre and also found in a few mountain areas in the southwestern United States.

Endemic: Referring to a plant or animal *species* that occurs naturally only in a restricted geographical area and is found nowhere else unless it has been transplanted.

Environment: All the external conditions, such as soil, water, air, and organisms, surrounding a living thing.

Erosion: The wearing away of areas of the earth's surface by water, wind, ice, and other natural forces.

Evergreen: A plant that does not lose all its leaves at one time. Most North American *conifers* are evergreens. *See also* Deciduous.

Evolution: The process of natural consecutive modification in the inherited makeup of living things; the process by which modern plants and animals have arisen from forms that lived in the past.

Fan delta: A fan-shaped deposit of rocks, gravel, and sediments that forms where the speed of water in a stream or other channel slows down abruptly, as at the foot of a steep *mountain* slope.

Flagging: A form of tree growth, characteristic of many trees at or near *timber line*, in which most of the elongation of branches is on the leeward side of the trunk. This lopsided growth form results from the drying and mechanical injury of buds on the windward side of the trunk.

Geographical race: *See* Subspecies.

Geology: The scientific study of the earth and the rocks that form it. A scientist who specializes in this study is a geologist.

Glacier: A large mass of ice that forms on high ground wherever winter snowfall exceeds summer melting. As snow and ice continue to accumulate at its center, the mass moves slowly downslope until it melts or breaks up. *See also* Ice age; Pleistocene.

Grassland: A *biome* that includes most of the United States west of the Mississippi River and east of the Rocky Mountains, where *climate* is wetter than in *deserts* but rainfall is insufficient to support the growth of forests.

Habitat: The immediate surroundings (living place) of a plant or animal; everything necessary to life in a particular location except the life itself.

Heath bald: A *bald* that is overgrown with shrubs of the heath family, especially rhododendron and mountain laurel. In the southern Appalachians, heath balds are known as "laurel slicks."

Herb: A flowering plant or fern that has a soft, rather than woody, stem.

Hibernation: A prolonged dormant or sleep-like state that enables an animal to escape the difficulties of survival during winter months in a cold *climate.*

Hudsonian zone: A *life zone* proposed by C. Hart Merriam and found at northern *latitudes* and high altitudes. The area usually is forested with spruce, fir, willows, and birches, and ends at *timber line.*

Ice age: The period in the earth's history characterized by the advance and retreat of continental ice sheets or *glaciers. See also* Pleistocene.

Kachina: A god of the Hopi Indians of Arizona. Kachinas are often represented as dolls which are given to Hopi children to acquaint them with their various deities.

Latitude: Distance north or south of the equator, measured in degrees.

Leader: The main shoot growing from the top of a tree with a single main trunk.

Life zones: The series of more or less parallel bands of distinctive plant and animal life resulting from the gradual change in *climate*, encountered as you move north from equator to pole, or up mountainsides in North America.

Lower austral zone: A warm but not entirely frost-free *life zone* encountered between the *tropical* and *upper austral zones* of C. Hart Merriam's classification. It is subdivided into a western *lower Sonoran zone*, characterized by saguaro cactus *deserts*, and an eastern *austroriparian zone*, characterized by live-oak and pine forests.

Lower Sonoran zone: A western subdivision of C. Hart Merriam's *lower austral zone.*

Mammal: Any member of the class of animals that includes elk, hares, man, and all other warm-blooded creatures except the birds. Mammals typically have a body covering of hair and give birth to living young, which are nursed on milk from the mother's breast.

Mixed forest: A *biome* characterized by the mixture of *coniferous* and *deciduous* trees.

Mixed forests extend across much of the northern United States and southern Canada just south of the area of *coniferous forests* but north of the area of *deciduous forests*.

Mountain: A natural elevation on the earth's surface, rising conspicuously above the level of the surrounding land.

Organic: Pertaining to anything that is or ever was alive or produced by a living plant or animal.

Peat: Partly decayed *organic* matter, usually sphagnum moss, formed in boggy areas where high acidity and lack of oxygen limit decomposition. *See also* Bog.

Plateau: An extensive flatland of high elevations, dissected by many steep valleys and *canyons*.

Pleistocene: Of or pertaining to the most recent period in the earth's history, roughly the past one million years. The period, also known as the *ice age*, includes at least four major retreats and advances of continental *glaciers*.

Population cycles: Rhythmic fluctuations in the abundance of certain animals, in which periodic increases in their numbers are followed by sharp and sudden declines. Although many animal *species* undergo regular population cycles, the cycles usually are most pronounced in *desert* and *tundra* areas.

Predator: An animal that lives by capturing other animals for food. *See also* Prey.

Prey: A living animal that is captured for food by another animal. *See also* Predator.

Rain forest: A very dense forest that grows as a result of exceptionally heavy rainfall throughout the year. Most rain forests occur in the tropics, but they may also be found in areas well north or south of the equator, where they are known as temperate rain forests. A famous example of such a forest

is preserved in Olympic National Park in the state of Washington.

Rain shadow: An area on the leeward side of a *mountain* barrier, receiving little rainfall.

Scavenger: An animal that eats the dead remains and wastes of other animals and plants.

Shrub: A woody plant, usually less than twelve feet tall and having many stems rising from the ground. *See also* Herb.

Specialization: The sum of the *adaptations* that enable a plant or animal to survive in a particular *habitat* or equip it for a particular mode of life.

Species (singular or plural): A group of plants or animals whose members breed naturally only with each other and resemble each other more closely than they resemble members of any similar group.

Subspecies (singular or plural): A group of individuals of the same *species* living within a more or less well-defined geographical area and differing slightly but consistently from individuals of the same species living elsewhere. A single species of plant or animal may include many subspecies.

Sunspots: Stormy areas that appear from time to time on the surface of the sun and are believed to influence climatic fluctuations on the earth.

Timber line: The upper limit of tree growth on a *mountain* or in northern regions; the line beyond which living conditions are too severe to permit the growth of trees. It is also called tree line. *See also* Flagging.

Transition zone: In C. Hart Merriam's system of classification, the *life zone* characterized by moderate temperatures and the intermixture of northern and southern forms of life. Typical vegetation is ponderosa pine forests in the West and mixed hardwood forests in the East.

Tropical zone: The southernmost zone in C. Hart Merriam's system of *life zones*. It is found in areas near the equator, where frost seldom or never occurs. In the United States it is found only at the southern tip of Florida.

Tundra: A *biome* characterized by short annual growing seasons, severe winters, and low precipitation. Tundra is found primarily beyond *timber line* in northern regions, where it is called *arctic* tundra; it also occurs above *timber line* on high *mountains* at lower *latitudes*, where it is called *alpine* tundra.

Upper austral zone: In C. Hart Merriam's system of classification, a *life zone* that is slightly cooler and often moister than the *lower austral zone* but warmer than the *transition zone*. It is subdivided into a western *upper Sonoran zone*, characterized by pinyon-juniper forest, and a more humid *Carolinian zone* in the East.

Upper Sonoran zone: A western subdivision of C. Hart Merriam's *upper austral zone*.

Volcano: An opening in the earth's crust through which gases, ashes, and molten material escape from the interior of the earth; a cone-shaped hill or *mountain* around such an opening and composed of material formerly expelled through the opening.

Wilderness: A tract of land, whether *mountain*, forest, seashore, *desert*, or any other, where man is only a visitor; an area where the original natural community of plants and animals survives in balance and intact, unaltered by mechanized civilization.

Bibliography

MOUNTAINS AND MOUNTAIN AREAS

BROOKS, MAURICE. *The Appalachians*. Houghton Mifflin, 1965.

KEPHART, HORACE. *Our Southern Highlands*. Macmillan, 1954.

LANE, F. C. *The Story of Mountains*. Doubleday, 1951.

MILNE, LORUS J., MARGERY MILNE, and THE EDITORS OF LIFE. *The Mountains*. Time, Inc., 1962.

PEARSALL, W. H. *Mountains and Moorlands*. Collins, 1950.

PEATTIE, RODERICK (Editor). *The Sierra Nevada*. Vanguard, 1947.

SPRAGUE, MARSHALL. *Great Gates: The Story of the Rocky Mountain Passes*. Little, Brown, 1964.

SUTTON, MYRON, and ANN SUTTON. *The Appalachian Trail: Wilderness on the Doorstep*. Lippincott, 1967.

THORNBOROUGH, LAURA. *The Great Smoky Mountains*. University of Tennessee Press, 1956.

ZIM, HERBERT S. *Rocky Mountains*. Golden Press, 1963.

PLANTS

COLLINGWOOD, G. H., and WARREN D. BRUSH. *Knowing Your Trees*. American Forestry Association, 1964.

CRAIGHEAD, JOHN J., FRANK C. CRAIGHEAD, and RAY J. DAVIS. *A Field Guide to Rocky Mountain Wildflowers*. Houghton Mifflin, 1963.

HARRAR, ELLWOOD S., and J. GEORGE HARRAR. *Guide to Southern Trees*. Dover, 1946.

RAVEN, JOHN, and MAX WALTERS. *Mountain Flowers*. Collins, 1956.

SARGENT, CHARLES S. *Manual of the Trees of North America*. Dover, 1965.

ANIMALS

BISHOP, SHERMAN C. *Handbook of Salamanders*. Hafner, 1962.

CAHALANE, VICTOR H. *Mammals of North America*. Macmillan, 1947.

CONANT, ROGER. *Field Guide to Reptiles and Amphibians*. Houghton Mifflin, 1958.

MURIE, OLAUS J. *A Field Guide to Animal Tracks*. Houghton Mifflin, 1954.

PALMER, E. LAURENCE. *Fieldbook of Natural History*. McGraw-Hill, 1949.

PALMER, RALPH S. *The Mammal Guide*. Doubleday, 1954.

POUGH, RICHARD H. *Audubon Land Bird Guide*. Doubleday, 1949.

POUGH, RICHARD H. *Audubon Western Bird Guide*. Doubleday, 1957.

STEBBINS, ROBERT C. *Field Guide to the Western Reptiles and Amphibians*. Houghton Mifflin, 1966.

STORER, TRACY I., and LLOYD P. TEVIS, JR. *California Grizzly*. University of California Press, 1955.

STUPKA, ARTHUR. *Notes on the Birds of Great Smoky Mountains National Park*. University of Tennessee Press, 1963.

ECOLOGY

BENTON, ALLEN H., and WILLIAM E. WERNER, JR. *Field Biology and Ecology*. McGraw-Hill, 1966.

BUCHSBAUM, RALPH, and MILDRED BUCHSBAUM. *Basic Ecology*. Boxwood Press, 1957.

KENDEIGH, SAMUEL C. *Animal Ecology*. Prentice-Hall, 1961.

MILNE, LORUS J., and MARGERY J. MILNE. *The Balance of Nature*. Knopf, 1960.

SMITH, ROBERT LEO. *Ecology and Field Biology*. Harper & Row, 1966.

GEOLOGY

FARB, PETER. *Face of North America*. Harper & Row, 1963.

FENTON, CARROLL L., and MILDRED A. FENTON. *The Fossil Book*. Doubleday, 1958.

FLINT, RICHARD FOSTER. *Glacial and Pleistocene Geology*. Wiley, 1957.

LONGWELL, CHESTER R., and RICHARD F. FLINT. *Introduction to Physical Geology*. Wiley, 1962.

PALMER, E. LAURENCE. *Fossils*. Heath, 1965.

PEARL, RICHARD M. *How to Know the Minerals and Rocks*. McGraw-Hill, 1955.

RHODES, FRANK H. T., and others. *Fossils*. Golden Press, 1962.

MOUNTAINEERING

BROWER, DAVID R. (Editor). *Going Light, with Backpack or Burro*. Sierra Club, 1953.

BROWN, BELMORE. *The Conquest of Mount McKinley*. Houghton Mifflin, 1956.

CLIMBING COMMITTEE OF THE MOUNTAINEERS. *Mountaineering: The Freedom of the Hills*. The Mountaineers, Seattle, Washington, 1960.

KING, CLARENCE. *Mountaineering in the Sierra Nevada*. Lippincott, 1963.

GENERAL READING

BUTCHER, DEVEREUX. *Exploring Our National Parks and Monuments*. Houghton Mifflin, 1960.

HILLCOURT, WILLIAM. *Field Book of Nature Activities and Conservation*. Putnam, 1961.

ISE, JOHN. *Our National Park Policy*. Johns Hopkins, 1961.

MATTHIESSEN, PETER. *Wildlife in America*. Viking, 1959.

MURIE, ADOLPH. *A Naturalist in Alaska*. Devin-Adair, 1961.

PETTINGILL, OLIN SEWALL, JR. (Editor). *The Bird Watcher's America*. McGraw-Hill, 1965.

STREET, PHILLIP. *Vanishing Animals: Preserving Nature's Rarities*. Dutton, 1963.

TEALE, EDWIN WAY. *The Wilderness World of John Muir*. Houghton Mifflin, 1954.

UDALL, STEWART L., *The Quiet Crisis*. Holt, Rinehart and Winston, 1963.

Illustration Credits and Acknowledgments

COVER: Mountain goat, Norman R. Lightfoot

ENDPAPERS: M. Woodbridge Williams, National Park Service

UNCAPTIONED PHOTOGRAPHS: 8–9: Bighorn sheep, Charlie Ott 66–67: The Adirondack Mountains, Laurence Pringle 110–111: Mountain Peaks, Olympic National Park, Bob and Ira Spring 148–149: Mountains, Glacier National Park, Lawrence R. Owen

ALL OTHER ILLUSTRATIONS: 10–11: Philip Hyde 12: Emil Muench 13: Dale A. Zimmerman 14: Mark Binn 15: J. M. Conrader 16: Robert W. Mitchell 17: Joe Van Wormer 18–21: Josef Muench 22: Harry Engels 24: Charles Fracé 25: Leonard Lee Rue 26–27: Eliot Porter 28: Josef Muench 29: Harry Engels 30–31: Josef Muench 33: Dick Kent Photography 34: Robert W. Mitchell 35: Josef Muench 36: Peter G. Sanchez 37: Norman R. Lightfoot 38: James W. Larson 39: Charles Fracé. 40: John S. Crawford 41: Tom McHugh, Photo Researchers 42–43: Norman R. Lightfoot 43: Leonard Lee Rue; Harry Engels; Thase Daniel 44: Patricia C. Henrichs 45: Leonard Lee Rue 46–47: Robert W. Carpenter 48: Norman A. Bishop 49: Bert Kempers 50–51: Patricia C. Henrichs 52: Robert W. Mitchell 53–54: Norman A. Bishop 55: Wilford L. Miller 56–57: Mark Binn 58–59: Charles Fracé 60: Mark Binn 61: Hans Zillessen, G.A.I. 63: Philip Hyde 64: Lawrence R. Owen 68–69: Mark Binn 70–71: Hans Zillessen, G.A.I. 72: Marjorie Pickens 73: Richard B. Fischer 74–75: Nick Drahos 75: Mark Binn 76–77: Nick Drahos 78–80: Laurence Pringle 81: Allan Roberts 82–83: Nick Drahos 84–85: Robert W. Carpenter 86–87: Marjorie Pickens 88: Stephen Collins 89: Alvah W. Sanborn 90: Jay Shuler 91: Hans Zillessen, G.A.I. 92–93: Raymond L. Nelson 95: Thase Daniel 96: Patricia C. Henrichs 97: Allan Roberts; Edmund J. Bucknall 98–99: Stephen Collins 100–101: Jack Dermid 102: Grant Heilman 103: Marjorie Pickens 104: Jack Dermid 105: Patricia C. Henrichs 106–107: William J. Jahoda 108: Marjorie Pickens 113: Bob and Ira Spring 114–115: Charlie Ott 116–117: Patricia C. Henrichs 118: J. M. Conrader; David C. Ochsner 119: Hans Zillessen, G.A.I. 120: Marjorie Pickens 121: Allan D. Cruickshank, National Audubon Society 122–123: Patricia C. Henrichs 124: Charlie Ott 125: Charlie Ott, National Audubon Society 126–127: Hans Zillessen, G.A.I. 128–129: John S. Crawford 130: Charlie Ott; James W. Larson 131: Kenneth Fink, National Audubon Society 132–133: Charles Fracé 134–135: Hal H. Harrison; Charles J. Stine 136–137: Patricia C. Henrichs 138–139: Lawrence R. Owen 140–141: Hiram L. Parent 142: Dale A. Zimmerman 144: L. J. Wanless, National Audubon Society 145: Guy J. Coheleach 146: Victor B. Scheffer 150–151: Jeppesen and Company 152: Robert W. Carpenter 153: Hans Zillessen, G.A.I. (after Pettingill) 154–155: Torrey Jackson 156: James L. Massey 157: Gene Hornbeck 158–159: Stephen Collins 160: Gene Hornbeck 162–163: Bert Kempers 164: Stephen F. Arno 165: Harry Engels 166: Norman R. Lightfoot 167: Charles Fracé 168: Richard B. Fischer 169: Bob Clemenz 170: Edmund J. Bucknall 171: Charlie Ott 172–173: Grant Haist 174–175: Bob and Ira Spring 176: John S. Flannery; Wayne P. Merry 177: Wayne P. Merry 178: Richard B. Fischer 179: Bob Clemenz 180: Coleman C. Newman 181: Willis Peterson; E. R. Degginger 182: Dana C. Morgenson 184: Hans Zillessen, G.A.I. 185: Bob Clemenz 186–187: Richard E. McGowan 188–189: Hans Zillessen, G.A.I. 190–191: Bob Clemenz 192: H. D. Wheeler 193: Grant Heilman 194–195: Coleman C. Newman 196: Wilford L. Miller, National Audubon Society 197: Peter G. Sanchez 198: Bob and Ira Spring 201: Patricia C. Henrichs 203–211: Charles Fracé 212–215: Mark Binn 216–220: Patricia C. Henrichs

PHOTO EDITOR: ROBERT J. WOODWARD

ACKNOWLEDGMENTS: *Although it is impossible to thank all the people who in various ways assisted in the preparation of this book, the author is especially grateful for the assistance of David S. Hamilton, who read the manuscript and offered many useful suggestions. The editors would also like to give special thanks to William W. Dunmire, C. Gordon Fredine, and William L. Perry of the National Park Service. Their careful scrutiny of the manuscript has resulted in a great many improvements in the book.*

Index

Abert's squirrels, 32
Acadia National Park (Maine), 203
Adams, Mount (N.H.), 111
Adams, Mount (Wash.), 183
Adaptations, 178, 221
  of bighorns, 40–41, 44
  of fish, 117, 119
  of hares, 123–124
Adirondack Forest Preserve (N.Y.), 74–77
Adirondack Mountains (N.Y.), 60, 70, 73–88
  altitude of, 71, 76, 79
  mountain climbing in, 79–81, 83–88
Alaska yellow-cedars, 194
Alaskan bighorns (Dall's sheep), 40, **43**, 130
Alder-leaved viburnum, 97
Alders, 23, **113**
Allegheny Mountains, 70, 119–120
Alpine, defined, 221
Alpine avens, **53**–54, 170
Alpine firs, 184, 194
Alpine forget-me-nots, **52**, **170**
Alpine sunflowers, 171
Alpine tundra, 53, 60, 86, 112, **168**, 194
Amphibians, 91, **132** (see also specific amphibians)
Andrews Bald, 100–101
Animals, 21, 29, 55–56, 99
  of bogs, 119–123
  desert, 13
  endemic, 90–91, 138
  nocturnal, 24, 44, 98, 188
  prehistoric, 90–92
  (See also specific animals and classes of animals)
Apache pines, 144
Appalachian Mountains, 59, 68, 70–73, 88–107, 119, 132
  age of, 71, 90–92
  ecological specialties of, 100–102, 104–105
  gaps in, 197, 199
  mountain climbing in, 93–94
  population isolation in, 137
  (See also specific mountains)
Appalachian Trail, 105–107, 111
Arctic, defined, 221
Arctic-alpine zone, 59–60, 79, 87, 138, 194, 221
Arctic tundra, 53, 116, 194
Arizona Snow Bowl, 34
Arizona walnut trees, 143
Ash trees, 23, 83, 105, 120
Aspens, **35**–**36**, 38–39, 56, 59–60, 65, 83, 120, 147, 169
Athabasca Glacier (Canada), **114**–**115**
Atlantic coastal plain, 98–99
Audubon's warblers, 29
Austral zones, 58–60, 221, 223, 225
Austroriparian zone, 58, 60, 221
Avalanche lilies, 184, 194
Avens, **53**–54, 170
Azaleas, 73, **102**, **108**, 192

Backpacking, 212–215
Baker, Mount (Wash.), **70**, 183

Bald eagles, 153, 156–**157**
Balds, **100**–102, 221
Balsam firs, 83, 85, 97, 105, 120, 137
Band-tailed pigeons, 144
Basswood trees, 105
Bear grass, 178–**179**, 188, 194
Bearberry willows, **88**
Bears, 34, 39–41, 56, 77, 109, **131**, 172–173, 188, 192, **210**
Beavers, 77, 167, 188, 192
Beeches, 81, 94, 120
Berthoud Pass (Colo.), 199
Big Bend National Park (Tex.), 203–204
Big Thompson Canyon (Colo.), 163
Bighorns (mountain sheep), 40–44, **55**–56, 130, 168, 172–173, 178
Biomes, 61, 221 (see also specific biomes)
Birches, 60, 77, 81, 83, 94, 105, 120, 169
  arctic, 88
Birds, 13, 36, 69, 132, 168–171
  of bogs, 121
  breeding of, 38–39, 84, 120–121, 168–169, 188, 194
  canyon-dwelling, 23–24, 27, 62, 143–144
  of eastern mountains, 77, 80–81, 83–86, 88, 94, 96–97
  Mexican species of, 24, **26**–**27**, 143–144, 147
  migratory, 152–156
  in pine forest, 29
  predatory, 13–14, 126, 152–156, 161, 168
  in pygmy forest, 14, 17
  (See also specific birds)
Bison (buffalo), 109, 157–159, 173
Bistort, 171, 188, 194
Black bears, 39–41, 56, 109, 172, 188, 192
Black cherry trees, 104–105
Black crowberry, 87–88
Black Hills (S.Dak., Wyo.), 162
Black locust trees, **209**
Black walnut trees, 104–105
Black-chinned hummingbirds, 23
Blackpoll warblers, 85
Black-tailed deer, 192, 194, **197**
Black-throated blue warblers, 97
Blanca Peak (Colo.), **71**
Block faulting, 183, 221
Blue gentians, 35
Blue grouse, 34, 36, **38**–**39**
Blue jays, 155
Blue Ridge Mountains, 70, 137
Blue Ridge Parkway (Va., N.C.), 106–107, 204
Bluebells, 35
Blueberry, 192
Bluets, 86
Bobcats, 14, 45, **104**
Bog orchids, 120
Bog rosemary, 120
Bogs, 119–123, 137, 221
Borah Peak (Idaho), **70**
Boreal, defined, 221
Boundary Peak (Calif., Nev.), **70**
Brasstown Bald Mountain (Ga.), **71**
Breeding, 84, 111, 117, 181, 196
  of amphibians, 133
  of birds, 38–39, 84, 120–121, 168–169, 188, 194

Bridled titmice, 143
Bristlecone (foxtail) pines, **44**, 47, 60, 85
Broad-tailed hummingbirds, 29, 32
Broad-winged hawks, 153–155
Brook trout, 117, 119
Brown creepers, 39, 97, 121
Brown trout, 119
Buck bean, **118**
Buckeyes, 105
Buffalo (bison), 109, 157–159, 173
Bullock's orioles, 23, 143
Bunchberry, **120**
Burkes Gardens (Va.), 120
Buttercups, 87, 171, 194
Butterflies, 13, 24, 86
  mountaintop, 111–112, 116

Cactuses, 12–14, 39, 47, 56, 58
  of canyons, 62–**63**
Cades Cove (Tenn.), 102
California condors, **211**
California quail, **208**
Calliope hummingbirds, 188
Calypso orchids, 173, **178**
Camas, 171
Camouflage, 36, 124, 169–170
Canaan Valley (W.Va.), 120
Canada geese, 155
Canada hemlocks, 96
Canada Mayflower, 97
Canada violets, 35
Canada warblers, 96
Canada yew, 120
Canadian zone, 59, 61–62, 65, 147, 194, 221
  of eastern mountains, 83, 84–85, 96–97, 99
Canyon wrens, 161
Canyons, 16, **18**–**21**, 23–24, 27–28, 32, 140, 143, 161, 163, 221
  fan deltas of, 104
  life zones of, 61–62, 138
Cardinals, 94–**95**
Caribou, **130**
Carolina hemlocks, **137**
Carolina wrens, 94
Carolinian zone, 58, 221, 225
Cascade Mountains, 69, 149, 183–184, 188–189, 194, **198**
Catkins, 221
Catskill Mountains (N.Y.), 149
Cave Creek Canyon (Ariz.), **142**–143
Ceanothus, 192
Cedar waxwings, 155
Cedars, 184, 194
Challenger, Mount (Wash.), **198**
Chestnut trees, **105**
Chickadees, 29, 39, 144
Chickweed, 54
Chihuahua pines, 144
Chipmunks, 24, 167
Chiricahua Mountains (Ariz.), **138**–**141**, 143–144, 147
Chiricahua National Monument (Ariz.), 139–141, 204
Chokeberry, 120
Cholla cactuses, 62

Chuckwallas, 62
Cinquefoil, 35
Circumpolar, defined, 221–222
Circumpolar distribution, 11
Clark's nutcrackers, 168, **204**
Clemson salamanders, 134, **136**
Climate (weather), 125, 132, 135, 186, 222
    of bogs, 122
    of canyons, 20–21, 62
    coastal, 189, 192
    of eastern mountains, 80, 81, 83, 86,
        99, 101
    of life zones, 56–60
    of mountaintops, 44, 48–53, 99, 112, 194
    prehistoric, 91–92
Clingmans Dome (Tenn., N.C.), **71**,
    100, 105
Coast Ranges, 189–192, 194, 196
Coati, 14
Coconino Plateau (Ariz.), 9–11, **14**,
    18–20, **28**–29, 32, 34, 59
Collared lizards, **13**, 62
Colorado River, 61–62, 65
Columbines, 35
Competition, 222
Condors, **211**
Coneflowers, **28**
Conies (pikas), **164–165**, 167–168,
    188, 192
Conifers, 222
Conservation, 222
Cooper's hawks, 153–154
Coronado National Forest (Ariz.), 139
Cougars (see Mountain lions)
Coves, 102, 104–105, 133, 222
Cowbirds, **81**
Coyotes, 14, 161, 192
Cranberries, **118**, 120
Cranberry Glades (W.Va.), 120–121
Cranesville Swamp (W.Va., Md.), 120
Crater Lake (Ore.), 183
Crater Lake National Park (Ore.), 204
Craters of the Moon National Monument
    (Idaho), 204–205
Creosote bushes, 143
Crevasses, **188–189**, 222
Crowberry, 87–88
Cumberland Gap (Va., Ky., Tenn.), 199
Cumberland Mountains, 70, 149
Cutthroat trout, 117

Dall's sheep, 40, **43**, 130
Darwin, Charles, 136–137
Death Valley National Monument
    (Calif., Nev.), 205
Deciduous, defined, 222
Deer, 14, 24, 32, 34–37, 39, 65, 77,
    128–129, 161, 172, 192, 194, **197**
    at margins of balds, 101
Delaware Water Gap (Pa.), 197, 199
Desert bighorns, 40, **43**
Desert ironwood, 12
Deserts, 12–14, 39, 43–44, 56–58,
    60–61, 138, 147, 222
Diapensia, **86–87**, 116
Dippers, **22**–23
Dogwood, 73
Doming, **68**
Donner Pass (Calif.), 199
Douglasfirs, 24, 34–36, 38–41, 44, 47, 59,
    65, 147, 184, 192, 194, **206**
Doves, 14
Dwarf buttercups, 87
Dwarf dogwood, **120**

Eagles, 153, 156–**157**, **160**–161, 194
Earthquakes, 67, 69
Eastern hemlocks, **137**

Ecologists, 60–61
Ecology, 10–11, 57, 222
    of balds, 100–102
Edge effect, 36, 38, 222
Elbert, Mount (Colo.), **70**
Elf owls, 13
Elk, 161, 167, 172, 188, 192
Encinal, 144, 222
Endemic, defined, 90, 222
Engelmann spruces, 44, 47, 60, 85, 167
Environment, 222
Erosion, 222
Estes Park (Colo.), 163
Everest, Mount, 186
Evergreens, 222
Evolution, 90–92, 222
    of isolated populations, 132, 135–139
    (See also Adaptations)
Extinction, 43, 77, 90, 105, 130, 155,
    157, 161, 210–211
    prehistoric, 91–92, 119, 132

Falcons, 153, **155**
Fan deltas, 104, 222
Faulting, **69**, 183, 221
Ferns, 35, 192
Field chickweed, 54
Finches, 121, 168–169, 178
    Galápagos, 136–137
Fir trees, 24, 59–60, 77, 105, 120,
    133–134, 147, 184, 192, **206**
    forests of, 34–36, 38–41, 44, 47, 65,
        83, 97, 194
    isolation of, 137
    timber-line, 85
Fish, 116–117, 119, **132** (see also specific
    fish)
Fishers, 77, 99
Flagging, 48–50, 194, 223
Flame azaleas, 102
Flickers, 13, 23
Flowers, 24, 29, 35–36, 73, 96, 107,
    116, 139, 167, 178, 184, 188
    of balds, 102
    of bogs, 120
    in canyons, 62, 65
    coastal, 192
    of cove forests, 105
    mountaintop, 53–56, 86–87, 97–98,
        170–171, 194
Flycatchers, sulphur-bellied, 143
Fog, 189
Folding, **68**
Forests, 44–47, 76–77, 81, 83–85,
    94, 97, 100, 107
    of arctic trees, 88
    at bog margins, 120
    coastal, 189, 192, 194, 197
    coniferous, 60–61, 83, 85, 96–97, 112,
        116–117, 133, 184, 194, 222
    cove, 104–105
    deciduous, 60–61, 72–73, 222
    of Douglasfirs, 34–36, 38–41, 44, 47,
        65, 167
    encinal, 144, 222
    in lower Sonoran zone, 58
    mixed, 223–224
    of ponderosa pines, 28–31, 32, 34, 47,
        144, 163, 167
    pygmy, 14, 16–17, 20, 47, 61
    of red spruce, 123, 125
    uppermost, 44–45, 47, 97
Forget-me-nots, **52**, **170**–171
Fossils, 216–220
Fox squirrels, 96
Foxes, 14, 17, **76**
Foxtail pines, **44**, 47, 60, 85
Franconia Notch (N.H.), 197
Fraser balsam firs, 97, 137
Fringed gentians, 173

Frogs, 24, 132
Frost, 58

Galápagos Islands, 136–137
Galax, 98
Gambel's quail, 14
Gannett Peak (Wyo.), **70**
Gaps, 197, 199
Gentians, 35, 170, 173
Geographical races (subspecies),
    136–137, 224
Geology, 223
Geums, 35
Geysers, 173
Giant daggers, **203**
Gila woodpeckers, 13
Gilded flickers, 13
Gilia, **29**, 54
Glacier Bay National Monument
    (Alaska), 205
Glacier lilies, 170, 184, 194
Glacier National Park (Mont.), 173,
    178–**179**, 205
Glaciers, 56, 71, 77, 112–117, 183–184,
    192, 223
    age of, 91–92, 98, 112, 116, 119,
        122–124, 132, 137, 173, 223
    mountaintop, 188–189
Glorieta Pass (N.M.), 199
Goldthread, 120
Golden eagles, 153, **160**–161
Golden plovers, 87–88
Golden-crowned kinglets, 121
Golden-mantled ground squirrels, **166–167**
Goshawks, 126, 153
Grace's warblers, 29
Grand Canyon, 28, 61–65
    life zones of, **61**–62, 138
Grand Teton Mountains (Wyo.), 69–70,
    172–173
Grand Teton National Park (Wyo.),
    172, 205–206
Grasses, 36, 49, 53, 65, 167, 178
    of balds, 100–102
    semidesert, 143
Grasslands, 60–61, 157, 161, 163, 223
Gray jays, 168
Gray-cheeked thrushes, 84–85
Gray-crowned rosy finches, 168–169, 178
Great Plains, 163, 167
Great Smoky Mountains National Park
    (Tenn., N.C.), 92–107, 124, 199, 206
    balds of, 100–102
    coves of, 102, 104–105
    population isolation in, 137
    salamanders of, 133–134
Green Mountains (Vt.), 35, 70, 88
Greylock, Mount (Mass.), **71**
Grizzly bears, 39, **131**, 172–173, **210**
Ground squirrels, 14, 17, 24, **166–167**, 178
Grouse, 34, 36, 38–39, 169–170
Guadalupe Mountains National Park
    (Tex.), 206
Guadalupe Peak (Tex.), **71**
Gulf Stream, 58

Habitats, 119, 223
Haleakala National Park (Hawaii), 206
Hares, 121, 123–127, 132
Harlequin quail, 144
Hawaii Volcanoes National Park
    (Hawaii), 206–207
Hawaiian geese, **210**
Hawk Mountain Sanctuary (Pa.), 152–156
Hawks, 14, 17, 126, 161, 168
    migration of, 152–156
Heath balds, 102, 223
Heather, 184, 188, 194

229

Heaths, 35, 98
Hemlocks, 81, 83, 96, 184, 192, 194
   isolation of, **137**
Henry Mountains (Utah), 68
Herbs, 49, 91, 94, 223
   of balds, 100–101
Hermit thrushes, 77, 83–85, 121, 147
Hibernation, 167–168, 223
Hickory trees, 72
Highlands salamanders, **136**
Hoh River, 192
Hood, Mount (Ore.), **70**, 183
Horned larks, 194
Horned lizards, 62
Hot springs, 173
Huachuca Mountains (Ariz.), 138, 144
Hudson Highlands, 67
Hudsonian zone, 59–60, 84–85, 194, 223
Hummingbirds, 23, 29, 32, 35, 188
Humphreys Peak (Ariz.), **70**

Ice age, 91–92, 98, 112, 116, 119,
   122–124, 132, 137, 173, 223
Indians, 14, 16–18, 56, 61, 101, 109,
   140, 167
   canyon-dwelling, 16, 18
   Hopi, 9–10
Insects, 13, 36, 101, 168
   canyon-dwelling, 23–24, 143
   mountaintop, 55–56, 86, 88, 111–112,
      116, 169
   parasitic, 29
   (See also specific insects)
Irises, 192

Jack rabbits, 14, 161
Jackson Hole (Wyo.), 172
Jacob's-ladder (sky pilot), **54**, 170
Jasper National Park (Canada), **114–115**
Jefferson, Mount (N.H.), 111
John Brook trail (N.Y.), 79, 81, 83
Jordan's salamanders, 133–136
Juncos, 86, 97, 144
Junipers, 14, 16–17, 20, 47, 58, 61–62

Kachinas, 10, 65, 223
Kaibab Plateau (Ariz.), 32, 62, 65, 71
Kaibab squirrels, 32, 65
Katahdin, Mount (Maine), **71**, 79,
   88–**89**, 106, 112
Katmai National Monument (Alaska), 207
Keene Valley (N.Y.), 79–80
Kennedy, Mount (Alaska), **70**
Kentucky warblers, 94
Kinglets, 39, 121, 147
Kings Canyon National Park (Calif.),
   183, 208–209
Kings Mountain (N.C.), 109
King's Peak (Utah), **70**
Kit foxes, 14
Kittatinny Mountains, 149, 152–156

Lakes, **74–75**, 77–**78**, 157, 172–173,
   183, 192
Lapland rosebay, **87**, **108**, 116
Largetooth aspens, 120
Larks, 194
Larkspurs, 192, 194
Lassen Peak (Calif.), 67, **70**, 183
Lassen Volcanic National Park
   (Calif.), 207
Latitude, defined, 223
Laurel, mountain, **73**

Laurel slicks (heath balds), 102, 223
Laurentian Highlands, 70–88 (see also
   Adirondack Mountains)
Leader shoots, **50–51**, 223
Le Conte, Mount (Tenn.), 71, 92–94,
   96–99, 132
Lemmings, 126
Lichens, **108**, **130**
Life zones, 57–62, 111, 147, 183, 221,
   223, 224–225
   of canyons, **61–62**, 65, 138
   of coastal ranges, 194
   of eastern mountains, 79, 81, 83–85,
      87, 94, 96–97, 99
Lilies, 170, 178, 184, 192, 194
Limber pines, 35, 59
Little chief hares (pikas), **164–165**,
   167–168, 188, 192
Little Tennessee River, 134
Live oaks, 58, **142–143**
Lizards, **13**, 62
Locust trees, 105, **209**
Lodgepole pines, 184
Longhorn cattle, 109, 158–159
Longs Peak (Colo.), **71**, 163
Loveland Pass (Colo.), 199
Lower austral zone, 58, 60, 223
Lower Sonoran zone, 58, 60–62, 138, 223
Lupines, 188, 192, 194
Lynxes, 126–130 (see also Bobcats)

McIntyre, Mount (N.Y.), 79
McKinley, Mount (Alaska), **70**, **130–131**
Magnolia trees, 105
Mammals, 14, 39–41, 44, 67, 88, 94,
   121, 132, 168, 223
   canyon-dwelling, 24
   mountaintop, 86, 99
   (See also specific mammals)
Mansfield, Mount (Vt.), **71**
Manzanita, 192
Maple trees, 72, 81, 94, 104, 120
Marcy, Mount (N.Y.), 71–72, 78–81,
   83–88, 93–94
   base of, 79, 94
   summit of, 78–80, 83–88
Marmots, 167–168, 178, 188, 192
Martens, 77, 99, **205**
Mazama, Mount (Ore.), 183
Meadows, alpine, 168–171, 178,
   184, 192, 194
Merriam, C. Hart, 57–61, 94
Mesquite, 12, 62, 143
Metcalf's salamanders, 133, **135–136**
Mexican chickadees, 144
Mexican juncos, 144
Mice, 14, 32, **99**, 156
Migration, 38–39, 87–88, 126
   barriers to, 32
   observation of, 152–156
Minks, 77, 205
Mississippi River, 90
Mitchell, Mount (N.C.), **71**, 105, 133
Mogollon Rim (Ariz.), 20, 28
Moles, 121
Montezuma Castle (Ariz.), 16
Moose, **89**, 172, **207**
Moraines, **114–115**
Moran, Mount (Wyo.), 172–173
Moss, 22, **122–123**, 137, 192
Moss campion, **171**
Mount McKinley National Park (Alaska),
   130–131, 207
Mount Rainier National Park (Wash.),
   184–189, 207–208
Mountain ash trees, 83
Mountain bluebirds, 168
Mountain chickadees, 29, 39
Mountain goats, 178–**181**, 188, 192
Mountain hemlocks, 194

Mountain laurel, **73**
Mountain lions, 39–**40**, 45, 65, 173,
   192, **196**, **211**
Mountain sheep (see Bighorns)
Mountains, defined, 224
Mourning warblers, 121
Mule deer, 14, 24, 32, 35–**37**, 39, 65, 172
Myrtle Peak (Tenn.), 98

Nantahala Mountains, 134
Nashville warblers, 121
Nenes (Hawaiian geese), **210**
Newfound Gap, 199
Notches, 197
Notre Dame Mountains (Quebec), 70
Nuthatches, 29, 97, 121

Oak Creek (Ariz.), **20–21**, 23–24
Oak Creek Canyon (Ariz.), **20–21**, 23–24,
   28, 62
Oaks, 58, **72**, 105, **142–144**
Oceans, 90, 117, 189–191
Ocotillo, 12
Old Faithful geyser, 173
Olive warblers, 144, 147
Olive-backed (Swainson's) thrushes,
   83–85, 121
Olympic National Park (Wash.), 189,
   192–196, 208
   Hurricane Ridge Road in, 192, 194
Olympus, Mount (Wash.), **70**, 192
Orchids, 120, 173, **178**
Organic, defined, 224
Orioles, 23, 143
Ospreys, 153–154
Otters, 77
Ouachita Mountains (Okla., Ark.), 162
Owls, 13, 17, 126
Ozark Mountains (Mo., Ark.), 162

Pacific Coast, 67, 117, 119, 132, 178
   (see also Coast Ranges)
Pacific silver firs, 194
Paintbrushes, 178, 188, 192
Painted redstarts, 23
Paleozoic era, 67
Paloverde, **12**
Panthers (see Mountain lions)
Paradise Glacier (Wash.), 188
Passes, mountain, 199
Peat, 122, 224
Peccaries, 14
Penstemon, 29, 194
Peregrine falcons, 153, **155**
Phoebes, 23
Pigeons, 144
Pigeon-wheat moss, 122–**123**
Pikas, **164–165**, 167–168, 188, 192
Pikes Peak (Colo.), **71**
Pine nuts, 16–17
Pine siskins, 39
Pine trees, 24, 28–32, 34–35, 58–62,
   144, 163, 167, 184, 194
   dwarfed, 14–17, 20, 47, 49
   of eastern mountains, 77, 81, 94
   in uppermost forest, 44
Pinkham Notch (N.H.), 197
Pinnacles National Monument (Calif.), 208
Pinyon jays, **17**
Pinyon pines, 14–17, 20, 47, 58, 61–62
Pipits, 45, 56, 168
Pitcher plant, 120
Plains, 60–61, 163, 167, 189
   coastal, 98–99
   midcontinental, 157, 161

Plants, 34, 36
  arctic, 87–88, 112, 116, 138
  of bogs, 119–123
  in canyons, 21, 61–62, 143
  endemic, 90, 138
  mountaintop, 53–55, 87, 97–99, 138
  prehistoric, 90–92
  reproduction of, 123, 137
  semidesert, 143
  (See also specific plants and classes of
    plants)
Plateaus, 224
Pleistocene epoch, 91–92, 116, 224
Plethodon salamanders, 90–91, 132–137
Plovers, 36
Polecat plant (scarlet gilia), **29**, 54
Polemonium (sky pilot), **54**, 170
Ponderosa pines, 28–31, 32, 34, 47, 59,
    62, 144, 163, 167
Ponds, 77–78, 167
Poppies, 192
Population cycles, 125–**127**, 132, 224
Porcupines, 44–**45**, 49, 172, 188
Prairie chickens, 36
Prairie dogs, 159, 161
Prairies, 60–61, 157
Predators, 17, 39–40, 55, 125–126, 224
  (see also Birds, predatory; specific
    predators)
Presidential Range (N.H.), 79
Prey, 224
Pronghorns, 161
Ptarmigans, 36, **169**–170, 178
Pumas (see Mountain lions)
Pygmy nuthatches, 29

Quail, 14, 144, **208**
Quaking aspens, 120
Quinault River, 192

Rabun salamanders, **136**
Raccoons, 77
Rain, 18, 80, 92, 167, 189, 192
Rain forests, 192–**193**, 224
Rain shadows, **189**, 224
Rainbow Curve Overlook (Colo.), 167
Rainbow trout, 117, 119
Rainier, Mount (Wash.), **69**, **70**, 183–189
Ravens, 101, 155, 168, 194
Red crossbills, 39
Red foxes, **76**
Red spruces, 85, 97, 120, 123, 125
Red squirrels, 96
Red-backed mice, **99**
Red-breasted nuthatches, 97, 121
Redbuds, 73
Redcedars, 184, 194
Red-cheeked salamanders, 133–**134**, **136**
Red-faced warblers, 24, **26**–**27**
Red-legged salamanders, 134–136
Red-shafted flickers, 23
Red-tailed hawks, 14, 153, **156**
Redwoods, 189, **192**
Reproduction, 123, 137 (see also
    Breeding)
Reptiles, 91, **132**, 139 (see also Lizards;
    Snakes)
Revolutions, geologic, 68
Rhododendron, 73, 87, **103**
  of balds, **100**, 102
  coastal, 192
Ringtails, 14, **24**–**25**
Roadrunners, 14
Rock sparrows, 161
Rock squirrels, 17
Rock wrens, 161
Rocky Mountain National Park (Colo.),
    163, 167–171, 208

Rocky Mountains, 43, **46**–**47**, 71, 139,
    162–178, 183, 189, 199
  Canadian, 39, 112, **114**–**115**
  northern, 171–173, 178
  Trail Ridge Road in, 167–171
  trout streams of, 119
Rodents, 17, 24, 56, 156 (see also
    specific rodents)
Rodgers, Mount (Va.), 71
Roosevelt elk, 192
Rose-breasted grosbeaks, 155
Rosecrown, 171
Ross's (alpine) avens, **53**–54, 170
Ruby-crowned kinglets, 39, 147
Ruffed grouse, 36
Rufous hummingbirds, 32, 188
Rufous-crowned sparrows, 161
Rushmore, Mount (S.Dak.), **71**

Sage grouse, 36
Saguaro cactuses, 12–14, 47, 56, 58
Saint Elias, Mount (Alaska), **70**
St.-John's-wort, 120
St. Lawrence River, 76
Salal, 192
Salamanders, 24, 99
  lungless, 90–91, 132–137
Salmon, 117
San Francisco Mountains (Ariz.), 9–12,
    14–20, 28, 30–62, 65, 83, 139
  base of, 20, 32
  life zones of, 56–60
  summit of, 34, 45, 53–57, 61, 138
Sand myrtle, 98
Sandia Peak (N.M.), **33**
Sangre de Cristo Mountains
    (Colo., N.M.), 32
Santa Catalina Mountains (Ariz.), 138
Santa Rita Mountains (Ariz.), 138, 144
Saxifrage, 35, 54
Scarlet gilia, **29**, 54
Scarlet penstemon, 29
Scavengers, 101, 224
Scott, Mount (Okla.), 156–157, 161
Sedges, 49, 53, 167
Sequoia National Park (Calif.),
    183, 208–**209**
Sequoias, 183
Serviceberry, 120
Shasta, Mount (Calif.), **70**, 183
Shenandoah National Park (Va.),
    67, 107, 209
Shrubs, 36, 83, 94, 97, 224
  arctic, 87
  of balds, 100, 102
  of bog margins, 120
  coastal, 192
  desert, **12**, 14
Sibbaldia, 54
Sierra Madres (Wyo., Colo.), 10, 139,
    144, 222
Sierra Nevadas (Calif.), 69, 149, 183, 199
Silver firs, 194
Silver-bell trees, 94, **96**, 105
Sitka spruces, 192, 194
Skunks, 14, 17
Sky pilot, **54**, 170
Slate-colored juncos, 86
Slide Mountain (N.Y.), **71**
Smuggler's Notch (Vt.), 197
Snakes, 14
Snipe, 121
Snow, 49, 112, 123, 164, 189,
    192, 194, 199
  melting of, 54–55, 86, 168–170, 184, 188
  permanent fields of, 56, 58, 178, 184
  as protection, 39, 50–51
Snowbird Mountains, 134
Snowshoe hares, 121, 123–127, 132

Snowy owls, 126
Sonoran Desert, 10, 12
Sonoran zones, 58, 60–62, 138,
    183, 223, 225
South Pass (Wyo.), 199
Spanish bayonet, 14
Sparrow hawks, 153–154
Sparrows, 86, **121**, 168–169
Specialization, 224
Species, 224
Sphagnum moss, **122**, 137
Springer Mountain (Ga.), **71**, 106
Spruces, 44, 47, 60, 120, 167, 192, 194
  of eastern ranges, 83, 85, 97
  as habitat, 123, 125, 133–134
Squirrels, 17, 32, 65, 96, 168
  flying, **98**–**99**, 121
Steller's jays, 29, 39
Sticky polemonium (sky pilot), **54**, 170
Stimson, Mount (Mont.), **70**
Streams, 16, 77, **82**, 96, 98, **103**, 197
  canyon, 22–24
  erosive action of, 71, 102, 104
  glacier, 188
  trout, 116–117, 119
Sublime, Point (Ariz.), 65
Subspecies, 136–137, 224
Sugar maples, 94, 104
Sugarlands Cove, 102, 104, 133
Sulphur butterflies, 24
Summer tanagers, 23
Sundew, 120
Sunspots, 126, 224
Swainson's hawks, 161, 168
Swainson's thrushes, 83–85, 121
Swallowtail butterflies, 24
Sycamores, 23, 143

Tamaracks, **119**–120
Tanagers, 23, 39, 143–**144**
Tassel-eared squirrels, 32
Tear-of-the-Clouds, Lake (N.Y.), **78**
Temperate rain forests, 192–194, 224
Teyahalee salamanders, 134, **136**
Thousand Islands (N.Y.), 76
Three-toed woodpeckers, 39, 86
Thrushes, 77, 80–**81**, 83–85, 121, 147
Timber (tree) line, 9, 11, 46–51, 60,
    100, 167, 192, 194, 224
  of eastern mountains, 78–80, 85–88, 111
  at low altitude, 173, 178, 184
Titmice, 143
Toads, 24, 132
Townsend's solitaires, 39
Transition zone, 51, 57–60, 194, 224–225
  of eastern mountains, 79, 81, 83–84,
    94, 99
Tree line (see Timber line)
Trees, 83, 100–101, 139, 143
  of coves, 104–105
  desert, 12–13
  dwarfed, 14, 16–17, 20, 47–51,
    88, 184, 194
  giant, 183, 189, **192**
  isolated populations of, 137
  of southern Adirondacks, 94, 96
  (See also Forests; specific trees)
Trillium, 192
Trogons, 144–**145**
Tropical zone, 58, 60, 225
Trout, 116–117, 119
Trumpeter swans, 172
Tuliptrees, 72, 105
Tundra, 47, 53, 60–61, 88, **116**–**117**,
    130, **168**, 194, 225
  butterflies of, 112, 116
  of eastern mountains, 86
Turkey vultures, 153, 155
Turkeys, **99**, 101, 109, 161

231

Uinta Mountains (Utah), 178, 183
Unicoi Mountains (Tenn.), 134
Upper austral zone, 58–60, 221, 225
Upper Sonoran zone, 58, 60–62, 183, 225

Valleys, 134–135, 162–163, 172–173,
  183, 188
  bogs in, 119–120
  eastern, 71, 90–91, 132
Varying (snowshoe) hares, 121,
  123–127, 132
Veeries, 83–84
Violets, 35, 86, 170
Volcanoes, 10–11, 67, 69, 183, 185, 225
Voles, 56, 99

Wallowa Mountains (Ore.), 149
Walnut Canyon National Monument
  (Ariz.), 16, 18–19
Walnut trees, 104–105, 142–143
Warblers, 24, 26–27, 29, 85, 94, 96–97
  of bogs, 121
  Central American, 144, 147
  migration of, 155
Washington, Mount (N.H.), 71–72, 79,
  88, 111, 116

Water gaps, 197
Water ouzels (dippers), 22–23
Water pipits, 45, 56, 168
Water shrews, 121
Waterthrushes, 121
Weasels, 17, 99
Weller's salamanders, 90
Western bluebells, 35
Western hemlocks, 184, 192, 194
Western redcedars, 184, 194
Western tanagers, 23, 39, 143–144
Western white pines, 184, 194
White ash trees, 105
White birches, 77
White camas, 171
White Mountain butterflies, 111–112,
  116
White Mountains (N.H.), 70, 88, 106–107,
  111–112, 116
White oaks, 105
White-crowned sparrows, 168
White-tailed deer, 36, 77
White-throated sparrows, 86, 121
White-winged doves, 14
Whitney, Mount (Calif.), 70
Wichita Mountains (Okla.), 149,
  156–159, 161
Wichita Mountains Wildlife Refuge
  (Okla.), 157–159, 161

Wilderness, defined, 225
Willows, 23, 59–60, 169
  arctic, 88
Wilmington Notch, 197
Wilson's thrushes, 83–84
Wind gaps, 197
Winds, 18, 34, 60, 189, 192
  gale, 48–49
  summit, 53, 86, 112, 169
Winter wrens, 77, 85–86, 97, 121
Winthrop Glacier (Wash.), 188
Wolf Creek Pass (Colo.), 199
Wolves, timber, 130
Wood oxalis, 97
Wood thrushes, 81, 83
Woodpeckers, 13, 39, 86
Wrens, 77, 85–86, 94, 97, 121, 161

Yellow birches, 94
Yellow-breasted chats, 96
Yellow-cedars, 194
Yellowstone National Park (Wyo., Mont.,
  Idaho), 173, 209
Yellowwoods, 94, 96, 105
Yosemite National Park (Calif.),
  182–183, 209
Yosemite Valley (Calif.), 182–183
Yuccas, 14, 62, 142